Landscape Management
for Water Savings

How to Profit from a Water Efficient Future

Sponsored by

 Municipal Water District of Orange County

 United States Bureau of Reclamation

 Metropolitan Water District of Southern California

 California Department of Water Resources

 Irvine Ranch Water District

 The California Landscape Contractors Association

Published by
Municipal Water District of Orange County
Author: Tom Ash
Water Efficiency Programs Manager
Horticultural, Water Rates & Conservation Products
CTSI Corporation, Tustin, California

Table of Contents

Introduction

"For the first time in recent history, Californians are finding that existing water management systems are no longer able to provide sufficiently reliable water service to users." (Department of Water Resources, DWR, California Water Plan, 160-98)

Water is the single most important resource for every aspect of green industry business. In California, driven in part by population growth and public policy, water is becoming a limited and expensive commodity. Water efficiency is becoming the rule for every type of user, be they commercial, industrial, or agricultural business, homes and community landscapes.

The *Landscape Management for Water Savings* was developed in conjunction with the California Landscape Contractors Association and the Municipal Water District of Orange County. The book materials have been reviewed by the California Landscape Contractors Association Resources Management Committee, representatives from the University of California Cooperative Extension, the United States Bureau of Reclamation, the Metropolitan Water District, the Irvine Ranch Water District, green industry companies and horticultural consultants. The book is produced by the Municipal Water District of Orange County with participation by the California Department of Water Resources (DWR), the Metropolitan Water District (MWD) and the U.S. Bureau of Reclamation (USBR). The goal of this publication is to assist the commercial and home landscape contractor and related green industry businesses, in understanding state and local water issues, how they affect landscape business, how to achieve water and resource efficient landscapes, and how the green industry profits by offering this service to customers.

There are many fine texts, manuals and guides for landscape maintenance, plant materials, plant care, design and irrigation. This handbook is <u>not</u> intended to replace those valuable references. Instead, this book describes how to integrate a wide variety of efficient landscape maintenance techniques along with the marketing of water efficiency to create greater business opportunity. Success helps public agencies meet increasing demands for water.

Water conservation and resource efficiency does not mean an end to business for green industry companies. Just the opposite. A water efficient landscape offers tremendous opportunities to sell higher valued services, introduce new plants, new technologies, make site upgrades and attract new business. It also means the green industry becoming partners with public agencies to offer solutions for living within California's water supply limits.

This handbook is not about eliminating landscapes to save water. It is about managing existing landscapes to be efficient so more water resources are available to meet population growth, economic development, and the public's desire for more landscapes. This handbook is designed to help green industry professionals understand the water supply future and how to adapt green industry businesses to meet new customer needs. This handbook advises promoting the role landscapes play in maintaining the value of homes and communities and describes that without water efficiency there will not be reliable supplies of water to meet the demands of population and economic growth estimated for California.

This elementary school student poster tells the whole story.

The Problem:
- Limited water supplies

Green Industry Goals:
- Maintain successful businesses in a state with limited water supplies
- Increase business opportunities
- Increase standards of performance and professional standing
- Become partners in the public policy-making process as it relates to water resource use

This handbook is:
- A practical guide to a healthier, more water efficient and cost effective landscape
- A primer on marketing water services to customers
- Another resource for green industry businesses to help manage landscapes efficiently and market those services to help increase business

CHAPTER 1

California Water and What It Means to Green Industry Business

This chapter summarizes water laws in the state and the direct impact public agencies have on water availability for landscapes.

The California Department of Water Resources (DWR) says , "For the first time in recent history, Californians are finding that existing water systems are no longer able to provide sufficiently reliable water service to users." (DWR California Water Plan, 160-98). The story is in the growing numbers. The population in California is expected to grow by 15 million people over the next 25 years, a 48% increase. Water demands are estimated to increase 37%. California also shares water from the Colorado River with other states. The population of these adjacent states is increasing, as is their need for water. Court actions have upheld the right of other states to take their share of water from the Colorado. That means California can expect to get less Colorado River water in the future.

California Urban Population by Hydrologic Region (millions) *(DWR, Bulletin 160-98)*

Region	1995	2020 *(projected)*
North Coast	0.6	0.8
San Francisco	5.8	7.0
Central Coast	1.3	1.9
South Coast	17.3	24.3
Sacramento River	2.4	3.8
San Joaquin River	1.6	3.2
Tulare Lake	1.7	3.3
North Lahontan	0.1	0.1
South Lahontan	0.7	2.0
Colorado River	0.5	1.1
Total	**32.1**	**47.5**

California's aqueduct system moves vast amounts of water to meet public need.

The California Department of Water Resources estimates that 'chronic' water shortages will happen soon after the year 2000. Without significant water conservation efforts, there will not be enough water to meet the needs of people, business and landscapes in the state in the near future.

The amount of water used for urban landscapes is currently estimated to be 5% of the total for all water used in the state. Every major customer group, including residential, institutional (schools, parks, etc.), commercial and industrial customers, use water for landscaping. For example, it is generally assumed that one-half of home water is used for irrigation. Currently, 82% of California's population lives in 'urban' areas. The desire and need for landscapes is high and will continue to grow as population grows. The need for water efficiency will also continue to grow.

And what about drought? Landscape water is the first water asked to be conserved during drought. Knowing how much water you use, how much water you need and how efficient a site is,

Industrial 8%

Unaccounted 10%

Institutional 7%

Commercial 17%

Residential 58%

Every major urban water use group listed above uses water for landscaping. It is estimated that one-half of residential water is used outside. Commercial and industrial customers use landscapes (and water) to enhance their business sites; institutional water includes schools and city parks, an important water necessity for the urban sector. 82% of California's population lives in "urban" areas. The desire and need for landscapes is high and will continue to grow with population increases.

(Source: DWR, Bulletin 160-98)

could mean the difference between the survival of that landscape, and your business, during drought.

The Role of Water Agencies

The California Water Code declares that, "the waters of the state are a limited resource subject to increasing demands"; "the conservation and efficient use of water shall be actively pursued"; and, "the conservation and efficient use of urban water supplies shall be a guiding criterion in public decisions."

(Left) California expects a population increase of 15 million people in 25 years.

(Below) Spanish missionary landscapes fit the dry "Mediterranean" climate.

State and local water agencies are charged with the task of delivering a reliable supply of water to meet all customer's needs, setting water rates, insuring the health, safety, economics and environmental resources of California. Water supplies and now water use are governed by an intricate system of federal and state laws. These laws, statutes, court decisions and contracts govern how water is developed, made safe for consumption and allocated for use.

State Water Use Efficiency: Article X, Section 2 of the California Constitution prohibits the waste of water. The use of water shall be exercised with a view to the reasonable and beneficial use thereof in the public interest and public welfare.

Urban Water Management Plan Act, AB 797 (1983): This act requires urban water suppliers to prepare water conservation plans, including estimating water use, identification of conservation measures and a schedule of implementation plans.

Water Conservation in Landscaping Act, AB 325 (1992): This act requires the adoption of a model water efficient landscape ordinance by cities and counties. The ordinance establishes methods of conserving water, water budget concepts, efficient designing, efficient irrigation and plant materials and site auditing.

Urban Best Management Practices MOU (BMPs, 1991): The BMPs established generally accepted practices among water suppliers that will result in water efficiency and the conservation of water. The 14 Best Management Practices are administered by the California Urban Water Conservation Council (CUWCC), an association of water agencies, environmental organizations and business groups such as CLCA.

CALFED (1992)/Proposition 204 (1996): The CALFED Bay-Delta Program is a cooperative effort involving the state and federal government with responsibilities for coordinating State Water Project and Central Valley Project water that's used throughout California. The major project areas include water use efficiency among urban and agricultural users.

The history of water laws that affect landscape water use date back to the California Constitution. Article X, Section 2 prohibiting the waste of water. The Urban Water Management Plan Act, AB 797 (1983), requires urban water suppliers to prepare water use and conservation plans. The Water Conservation in Landscaping Act, AB 325 (1992), requires the adoption of a model water efficient landscape ordinance by cities and counties. The ordinance established methods of conserving water in the landscape, measuring water budgets, requiring efficient site design,

Current State Best Management Practices (BMP's, 1998)

1. Residential Water Survey (audit) Programs *(home landscape efficiency)*

2. Residential Plumbing Retrofit

3. System Water Audits, Leak Detection and Repair

4. Metering with Commodity Rates for All New Connections and Retrofit of Existing Connections *(leading to landscape water budgets)*

5. Landscape Conservation Programs and Incentives *(commercial landscapes with water budgets)*

6. High Efficiency Washing Machine Rebate Program

7. Public Information Programs

8. School Education Programs

9. Conservation Programs for Commercial, Industrial, and Institutional Accounts *(commercial landscapes, metered and unmetered)*

10. Wholesale (Water) Agency Assistance Programs

11. Conservation Pricing *(rewarding water use efficiency)*

12. Conservation Coordinator

13. Water Waste Prohibition

14. Residential Ultra Low Flush Toilet (ULFT) Replacement Programs

(Left) State laws seek to allocate water resources for protection and equity.

(Below) Inefficient water use will negatively impact California's economy.

efficient irrigation systems and site auditing. The latest public policy decisions center on Best Management Practices (BMP's) that will establish water use standards (water budgets) for landscapes (and other water users) across the state.

Why is knowledge of water laws important for the green industry? Because decisions are being made at the federal, state, regional and local levels that directly impact the designs of landscapes, the water available for landscapes and even if water will be available for new developments to be built. In the list above, BMP's 1, 4, 5, 9 & 11 will have a direct impact on home and commercial landscapes. Customers that pay water bills will be asked to use water efficiently. Those same customers will look to the landscape professional to manage and maintain the landscape under these new standards of water efficiency.

With limited water supplies and increasing population, water use, or water budgets, will be set by state mandates. In practical terms, it means that each and every water user will be required to be efficient and meet water budgets in the future. Every water customer will have "Best Management Practices" to live and work by.

For the green industry, a reliable supply of water is the key to business success. The green industry opportunity, then, is to know the state and local water supply issues and offer services that help customers have healthy, attractive and resource efficient landscapes that meet the local public needs and standards. The green industry can offer solutions that maintain and beautify landscapes while meeting water budgets. Being part of the solution to California's water supply problems will mean new business opportunities for green industry businesses.

The legislative system is in place. Public agencies are moving forward to implement water efficiency standards. What will the response of your business be to the challenge of landscape resource efficiency?

CHAPTER 2
Property Value, Plant Use and Marketing for the Water Efficient Landscape

This chapter offers contractors tips and ideas they can champion in the pursuit of expanding business, raising industry standards and marketing the value of resource efficient landscape services to prospective customers.

"There are always opportunities through which businessmen can profit handsomely, if only they recognize and seize them." J. Paul Getty

Landscaping as a Property Value Enhancement

We think it. We know it. Now we need to say it and sell it over and over again. Plants and landscapes make a significant contribution to the value of urban life, our homes, streets and communities. Picture a home, a street or a community without trees, grass and flowers. Landscapes define where we live and the quality of our local environment.

Landscape professionals can and should help their customers link the value of property with the quality of landscapes. Landscape contractors do not just mow, blow and go, they "manage assets," as one contractor in southern California likes to say. Managing a home or business landscape "asset" implies a great trust on the part of the customer that has been placed in the hands of the landscape company professional. Asset management requires sophistication, attention to detail, consistent monitoring of trends, be they weather or market changes, keeping up with the latest technology and being responsive to customer needs. Sounds like Wall Street, but it applies just as easily to green industry businesses. If we believe in the value of landscapes, we must make the case with hard numbers, that quality installation, maintenance and upgrades keep up with market trends and achieve efficiency. That service, to maintain high quality landscapes, is what's most valuable to the customer.

Functional Use of Plants

How many times are homes, businesses and streets built where we immediately look for plants to "soften," "mitigate," "screen" and "enhance" the impact of the urban setting? Every single time! Plants and landscaping perform that task.

One of the great benefits of plants is their functional use. Turf is necessary for recreation, walking, sitting, picnicking, etc. Trees screen and shade. Shrubs and groundcovers screen and provide color. All plants help control soil erosion. Sometimes, unfortunately, plants are used improperly. Poor landscape design leads to excessive costs, high water and high resource inputs, difficult maintenance and a low valued investment for the customer. Evaluate the landscape site for its functional needs. Is the landscape meeting those needs? How can it better meet customer needs? Look for the most resource efficient techniques to fit the functional need requirements for the site. That is the landscape that becomes a high valued asset for the customer

Evaluating the landscape for its best functional use with the right amount of water, fertilizer and

Benefits of landscapes for homes and cities:

● Increased Property Values
● Increased Air and Environment Quality
● Energy Savings from Shading Urban Heat Islands
● Increased Wildlife Habitat
● Positive Psychological Impact People
● Major California Industry

Landscapes are important. Promo the need for landscapes. Water to maintain landscape plants is esser

Functional Plant Uses:

● Trees that shade buildings, stre and parking lots (heat islands)
● Shrubs that fit into planter spac without pruning
● Turf for activity or traffic areas
● Covering slopes to reduce eros
● Creating an aesthetic image or comfort zones
● Colorful and edible gardens
● Restoration for wildlife habitat

labor, is another opportunity for understanding the true costs and benefits of a site and potentially increasing its value and adding new business.

Environmental Benefits of Plants

People generally recognize the environmental value of plant materials. However, poor landscape design with the wrong plants in the right places maintained with excessive water can offset the benefits of landscapes for the customer and contribute to environmental deterioration. Poor landscape practices increase green waste production, increase chemical use, use water inefficiently, increase soil erosion and produce unhealthy, unproductive, unattractive and more costly landscapes.

High quality, water efficient, healthy and environmentally sound landscapes go hand in hand. Those high quality landscapes don't just happen. It requires knowledge, sophistication, consistent monitoring and pride to deliver that high quality service. The environmentally sound, water efficient landscape sets a higher standard of value in the eye of the customer. Industries across the country have benefited in the marketplace by becoming more sensitive to the environment and marketing their environmental ideals. The green industry is the industry of environment. The green industry can and should use environmental quality as a guide to creating resource efficient landscapes for customers. The green industry can use environmental benefits as another tool to market high quality services to customers.

"New" Business

Where is new business for the green industry? With California's population predicted to grow by nearly 50% over the next 25 years, meeting growth demands will mean "new" business if there is enough water to sustain expected development.

New landscapes, based on state legislation, will need to be more water efficient. The majority of landscaping in the state (found in existing homes, communities and commercial landscapes) needs to be made as water efficient as possible. Why? All Californians will be asked to be water efficient. Landscapes will be one of the first "water users" to be required to meet water budgets to save water. Making landscapes efficient will certainly mean the need for new equipment and plant materials. But the main need will be for people with the ideas, the knowledge and the attitude to help customers become water efficient.

The development of "new" business, expanding markets and increasing profit margins is the continuous challenge for every business in every industry. The greater demand for water and resource efficiency opens a door for green industry businesses who are ready and willing to answer the challenge. California's population projections and water demands show this challenge will **never** go away.

Landscapes are an important community and business enhancement.

What is Evapotranspiration (ET)?

Evapotranspiration (ET) is the combined process of both evaporation from the soil and plant surfaces and water transpiration through plant materials. The measurement of water evaporation from the soil and transpiration through plant leaves by weather stations provides daily, weekly and monthly water replacement values. ET is measured in terms of inches of water per day, week, month or year. ET changes constantly with the weather.

What is a Water Budget?

- A water budget sets targets for water use in a landscape. Water budgeting is the practice of applying only the amount of water required by plants for healthy growth and appearance.
- The water budget concept was developed by researchers, green industry professionals and public agencies. It was utilized as the guide for making landscapes efficient through the state Water Conservation in Landscaping Ordinance (AB 325) in 1992.
- The water budget standard is based on reference evapotranspiration (ETo) as measured by California Irrigation Management Information System (CIMIS) weather stations. The water budget for a site can be determined by the following equation, including the weather (ET), the crop coefficient (Kc), where Kc is the relative water requirement of the plant species to be irrigated, a factor for irrigation efficiency and the site size. The equation for a site water budget is written as

$$\frac{(ET)\ (Kc)\ (Area)}{(irrigation\ efficiency)} = Site\ water\ budget$$

Keys to Better Business in a Water-Short State:

- Knowledge of the issues and public policy affecting green industry business
- Willingness to learn and use plant/water research, local ET, and the use of advanced cultural practices to optimize resource efficiency
- Business attitude of seeking to provide the best possible service to customers by delivering water and resource efficient landscapes

The Green Industry Opportunity: Making Water Efficiency Work for You – Case Studies from the Commercial, Homeowner Association, City and Landscape Markets

This chapter presents real world examples of landscapes and management practices that have resulted in efficient and high quality landscapes.

Population growth will require water efficiency in new development.

Water is becoming a limited resource in California due to the increasing demands of every water using group. State legislators have enacted regulations aimed at the efficient use of water by all water users. Local water agencies will pass along water use targets by enacting ordinances, policies or pricing structures aimed to conserve water supplies. To some, this may seem a reason to leave the green industry. Others will seize the opportunity to provide higher valued services and profit from meeting customer needs in a changing market.

Will there be enough water for urban landscapes? Yes! If a wide variety of water supply projects are implemented, including the expanded use of recycled water and increasing the ability to move and store water during wet periods. However, water conservation and meeting water efficiency targets will always be key to insuring a reliable supply of water for urban landscapes.

Will urban landscapes dry up under such regulations? Will business suffer? BMPs, water budgets and conservation pricing is already happening in communities in California. The example of Irvine offers a very positive outlook for green industry business in a water budget future:

Landscape water use decline is attributed to conservation pricing (water use above the ET water budget is priced at increasing block rates), financial incentives and education programs for customers and landscape professionals. Over 7,000 acres of landscape areas are measured, have separate meters and are billed according to how well they meet a real time 100% ET water budget (historical ET for the area is 4.1 AF/AC/Yr). A 43% increase in landscape water efficiency (water savings) from 1990 to 1997 has been achieved. The community is considered green and lush and maintains high property values.

"New" business for the green industry was created in this community specifically to address landscape water use and efficiency standards, based on ET water budgets, set by the public agency. What has been the impact of the water budget system on the landscape water users in Irvine?

The Winners: The bill paying customers. They have significantly reduced water bills and gained healthier landscapes at the same time. All local businesses, including commercial, manufacturing, nursery growers, agricul-

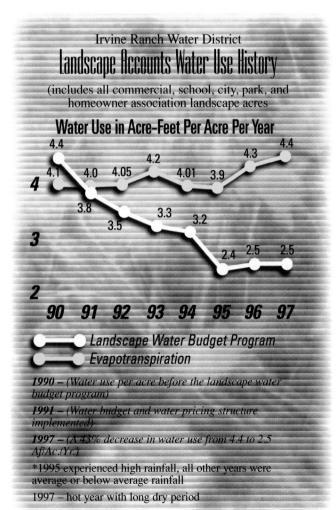

Irvine Ranch Water District
Landscape Accounts Water Use History

(includes all commercial, school, city, park, and homeowner association landscape acres

Water Use in Acre-Feet Per Acre Per Year

4.4 4.1 4.0 4.05 4.2 4.01 3.9 4.3 4.4

3.8 3.5 3.3 3.2 2.4 2.5 2.5

90 91 92 93 94 95 96 97

— Landscape Water Budget Program
— Evapotranspiration

1990 – (Water use per acre before the landscape water budget program)

1991 – (Water budget and water pricing structure implemented)

1997 – (A 43% decrease in water use from 4.4 to 2.5 Af/Ac/Yr.)

1995 experienced high rainfall, all other years were average or below average rainfall

1997 – hot year with long dry period

Landscapes add to property value and environmental quality.

ture, the city, the school district and homeowners benefit from paying the lowest water rates in the county. Water rates have not increased in five years, and the low water rates are a direct result of district management and water efficiency being practiced in the area.

The Water District: Meets state guidelines (BMP's) for efficient water use among customers. The district has helped create more knowledgeable customers with a water conservation ethic and actively partners with customers and the green industry to achieve low water bills.

The Landscape Contractor: Contractors have become part of the water conservation solution. Local contracting companies profit from water district incentive programs that help pay for upgraded irrigation systems and landscapes. Landscape Contractors use more sophisticated tools with which to manage their sites. They use successful, water efficient sites to market their skills and services to potential new customers. The impact of setting and meeting water efficiency standards in Irvine has been a financial and marketing benefit to contractors that recognize water efficiency as a business opportunity.

The following real life case studies show how specific customers and contractors in homeowner associations, homes, cities, and business parks have responded to regulations for water budgets.

Case Study No. 1

Commercial, City and Homeowner Association Case Studies

25 Acre Homeowner Association landscape, 90% turf, 25 years old

The Problems: $90,000 in over-allocation (ET) water penalties in one year; poor turf appearance; little landscape color; woody and heavily pruned shrubs; street pavement erosion due to water run-off.

The Goals: Use water at or below the water budget allocation (ET), eliminate water penalty costs, improve turf appearance, increase site color, reduce water damages to pavement, fences and structures.

The Solution:
- Create a site master plan for phasing of landscape upgrades
- Upgrade old irrigation controllers and make spray heads uniform
- Convert the water source to recycled water
- Manage for the predominate warm season turf species, Bermuda
- Install a centralized irrigation control system
- Irrigate turf and shrub areas at proper ET/Kc level
- Read meters weekly to track water use and schedule irrigation to replace water loss
- Read meters and compare to ET to help identify leaks quickly
- Phase-out the removal of sheared shrubs and phase-in selective pruning
- Remove over-planted trees to reduce yearly trimming costs and improve turf conditions
- Rewrite landscape contract to specify high valued maintenance tasks and water management requirements

completed project designed to show savings and payback in water and maintenance savings in six years.

The irrigation system equipment upgrades and recycled water conversion have been completed. A central irrigation control system is operating and schedules are per the ET based water budget allocation. Over-water use penalty costs for the customer have been eliminated. Trees have been removed and new, more appropriate species have been installed. New turf maintenance and cultural practices have been implemented. The landscape contract has been rewritten and became the guide for bidding and maintenance work.

The Winners: The homeowner association. The owners gain a more attractive and cost-effective landscape with a six year payback time. Residents are improving their own gardens, showing newfound pride in the overall association landscape upgrades.

The Water District: Sees a 52% decrease in water use, saving 17 million gallons of potable water per year.

The Landscape Contractor: Performs over $750,000 worth of "extra" upgraded work; gains an updated irrigation system with which to manage the site; participates with the customer and water district to achieve site water efficiency.

Case Study No. 2

(Left) Street erosion due to landscape water inefficiency.

(Above) Before: No color, plants don't fit planting space, tree root damage.

4.5 Acre Homeowner Association, 205 condo units, small landscape planters consisting of trees, shrubs and groundcovers, little turf, 15 years old

The Problems: High water bills and over-allocation (ET) use; generally unattractive landscape with bare soil spots; weeds; no flower color; severely sheared shrubs; over 200 trees with disease and/or causing hardscape damages from roots; streets and parking areas with paving erosion from water run-off; frequently leaking irrigation system; parked cars often sprayed by irrigation system; generally poor community aesthetics.

The Goals: Convert spray irrigation system to drip irrigation; renovate and replace plant materials; remove diseased trees; eliminate hardscape and street damages; add color, increase community shade and overall community aesthetics.

After: A complete site retrofit provides color, low maintenance and helps property value.

The Solutions:
- Produce a site master plan that addressed each of the listed problems
- Received a $50,000 zero-interest loan from the water district to begin the project
- Used close collaboration between association board, landscape committee, residents, property manager, water agency and landscape contractor during every step of the project

The Results: A total site renovation; irrigation retrofit from spray to drip; a landscape upgrade including over 6,000 new container plants, 500 flats of groundcovers, at a total cost of $85,000; a new look for the association; project payback of 6.5 years; water use potential of 50% to 70% of the local ET and reduction of high water bills; elimination of hardscape damages (a hidden cost of landscape and water inefficiency to the association) due to poor original plant and irrigation design, water overspray and runoff.

The Winners: The Homeowner Association. Gains a colorful new look while eliminating landscape induced water and hardscape damages; water bills reduced; tree/hardscape problems eliminated; overall landscape costs reduced.

The Water District: Gains water efficiency from a historically wasteful site, saving 2.6 million gallons per year.

The Landscape Contractor: Performed an "extra" $85,000 worth of work and gained a new contract with higher valued specifications for water management and cultural practices; the site is efficient and needs less contractor time for constant "fixes"; the landscape no longer needs to be "managed by crisis".

HOA park that meets water budget

ase Study No. 3

Homeowner Association, 38 landscape acres, 4,000 single family and condo homes, 85% turfgrass, 10 years old

The Problems: Over $100,000 in over water budget (ET) penalty charges over 3 years; unusable, muddy parks; algae-stained stucco walls; stunted tree growth; consistent turf "hot spots".

The Goals: Eliminate water use penalties, reduce water over-spray on walls; improve overall turf and tree health and achieve goals with no turf or plant material changes.

The Solutions:
- Use of ET water budget irrigation scheduling
- The use of cultural practices to improve turf quality, including regular aeration, turf top dressing with organic material, grasscycling and root development techniques
- Contracted for water management services with an outside specialist
- Instituted a preventative irrigation system maintenance program including pressure regulation and spray head adjustments, weekly meter reading, weekly scheduling adjustments and retro-fitting of improper spray heads

The Results: Water use reduced 32%; water penalties eliminated; parks are dry and playable; algae-stained wall damages eliminated; turf "hot spots" reduced; hardscape damages and costs were reduced; the turf has more uniform appearance and the parks are no longer muddy; accomplished with no change of plant materials.

The Winners: The homeowners association. Enough money was saved to lower resident dues and build new tennis courts;

The Water District: Gains water efficiency with a large customer and saves 15.8 million gallons per year without any financial incentives invested in the site.

The Landscape Contractor/Consultant: Provides irrigation upgrades that make site management easier; learns and utilizes advanced cultural practices to improve turf water efficiency and appearance. The contractor becomes a major player in solving customer problems and saving customer dollars.

ase Study No. 4

Business Center Landscape Study, 8 acre study site (128 acre business park landscape), 95% turf, turf streetscapes on modest slopes with compacted clay soil; 7 years old.

The Problems: A high tech, exclusive business park with 128 acres of turf-oriented streetscapes and themed entrances with 50,000 cars passing through daily. When the water budget allocation system was adopted in 1991, the landowner experienced high water penalty costs. Turf, even with significant over-watering, was showing consistent "hot spots" causing unacceptable turf appearance. The landscape contractor blamed site problems on the "unfair" water budget allocation system imposed by the water district.

The Goals: Conduct a study to determine if the site could meet the 100% ET water budget; create a management plan to eliminate over-allocation water penalties; improve turf health and appearance. The site owners wanted to maintain the original plant design.

(Below) Study of irrigation efficiency, root depth, maintenance and scheduling.

(Bottom) Business park streets meeting ET water budgets.

The Solutions:

● Conduct a comprehensive, independent study on the ability of the sites turf streetscapes to meet 100% ET water budget allocations. (The study was conducted over a one year period covering representative landscape hydrozones, 48 test sites in all, across 8 acres of the business park.)

● Analyze site test results and compare to visual appearance rankings

● Develop detailed maintenance specifications for water and turf management

The Results: All 48 test sites met or used less irrigation water than the 100% ET water budget allocation standard set by the water district. Test sites that incorporated advanced cultural practices and ET water budget irrigation scheduling provided the highest quality and best looking turf, increasing turf root depth by 66%. Water use on the test sites was reduced 51% from previous years. Turf appearance and health is better at the end of the study with a 90% of ET water budget than during years when 200% of the ET was applied.

The property management company incorporated the water management and recommended cultural practices into maintenance contracts across the entire 128 acre business complex landscape. The water efficiency program has reduced water bills by $1.3 million from 1993 to 1996. It has meant the saving of 53 million gallons of water in four years. The turf is healthier with deeper root systems and less unsightly "hot spots". There is also reduced hardscape damages to streets and parking lots from water run off and overspray.

The original site contractor, claiming that water budget allocations were not adequate to meet site needs, was replaced. The new site contractor has a positive attitude toward using ET water budget irrigation scheduling to manage a landscape. This same contractor has been rewarded by the landowner with a doubling of landscape acreage under their management. The new site contractor has continued to improve on the business center water efficiency success and added "new" business to the books.

The Winners: The landowner/developer. The owner gains a more cost effective landscape. With a more efficient landscape site, the developer is able to keep leases and site costs lower for an improved competitive advantage. The improved turf health and overall landscape appearance is believed by the developer to be key to marketing the office space to potential business tenants. The developer is now confident, based on the study results, that this and any landscape site can be irrigated efficiently, meet 100% ET water budgets and have high quality appearance at the same time. Some $1.5 million in water bills has been saved for the site owner since 1994.

The Water District: Gains the confidence of the areas major developer that a water budget can meet the needs of an existing turf landscape. For all customers and contractors in the water district, the study proves the ability of ET water budget allocations to meet the needs of difficult landscape sites. The water district gains the savings of 11.3 million gallons of water per year in the business park.

The New Landscape Contractor: They have significantly increased acreage under their management, and now actively promote the water management abilities of the company.

The Loser: The previous landscape contractor. Lost a highly visible 128 acre site contract. The water use prior to the study was 50%-100% over the 100% ET water budget allocations for the site. The contractor consistently blamed the ET water budget allocations as "not enough water" to adequately maintain the site. The real site problems turned out to be (1) avoided irrigation system maintenance, (2) avoided cultural practices based on plant needs, and (3) excessive water use that damaged plant root systems.

Historical Water Use Attitude:

Excessive water has traditionally been used to compensate for or mask poorly designed, old, inefficient or poorly maintained irrigation systems.

New Water Use Attitude:

With the need to make urban water use as efficient as possible, water will no longer be able to be used to cover-up the weaknesses of a landscape design, irrigation system or poor management. Water will be applied at the right level, weather (ET) x plant requirements (Kc) for each hydrozone in the landscape. If site irrigation weaknesses appear, it is understood that system upgrades and/or management changes are needed. These upgrades and/or changes begin the process of the contractor helping to solve problems in the landscape for the customer. Water efficiency means more work, higher valued work, more irrigation materials and potentially more plants sold and installed, healthier and more attractive landscapes for contractors to promote. Recognize and practice efficient water management and promote that valuable service to increase business opportunity.

City Landscape Water Management Program, 350 water meters, 558 acres or streetscapes, parks and parkways; new to 30 years old; a variety of contractors perform City maintenance work

The Problems: Over water use. In 1994 alone the City had accumulated $184,000 in water penalty costs (water used over 100% ET budget); the wasted water, some 70 million gallons, caused damages to streets and the landscape; the turf streetscapes often exhibited "hot spots"; trees were suffering or stunted; City costs were going up while City revenues, due to a slow economy, were going down.

The Goals: Eliminate or reduce water use penalty costs; improve landscape appearances; implement more sustainable and less costly practices.

The Solutions:
- The City initiated a comprehensive water management plan that tracked the irrigation scheduling of every landscape water meter on a monthly basis
- Irrigation schedulers (city staff and contractors) were held accountable for managing water at 100% ET levels (private contractors going over the 100% ET water budget are responsible for paying water penalties)
- Upgraded training of water managers
- Revised maintenance contracts to specify cultural practices that provided improved plant health, deeper turf roots, fertilizer reductions, green waste recycling, water and resource efficiency
- New street landscape design guidelines prioritize greater sustainability, green waste reduction and water efficiency

The Results: Water use has been reduced 46%; water bills have stabilized compared to other utility costs; landscape appearance and health has been maintained; City staff understands that water budgets can be met; landscape specifications have been rewritten to include more advanced cultural practices (and bid at virtually the same price as previous contracts); City realized that well trained people were more important to achieving goals than technology; City realized that 80% of water penalties and water damages to streets came from areas of turfgrass and overhead spray in street medians; City identified that an effective maintenance program never ends and should never cut corners; use of soil tests reduced fertilization 60%; City found that proactive programs are more cost effective and preferable to reactive programs to avoid landscape problems and costs.

The Winners: The City. They have gained a more sophisticated and cost effective approach to understanding how best to maintain their valuable landscapes. They have maximized appearance and minimized budgets while City taxpayers see more colorful and diverse streetscapes. The City can justify these efforts by the reduction of costly erosion on streets and reduced water bills.

The Water District: Sees 70 million gallons of water saved per year. City landscape water efficiency helps keep water rates low for all customers.

Future City Landscape Contractors: They gain precise City contracts on which to bid and perform work.

The Losers: The landscape contractor who under-bids to get the work and can't profit due to the specialized contract responsibilities; contractors who don't meet water budget allocations pay water penalty charges and ultimately lose City contracts.

Home Landscape Case Studies

Case Study No. 1

A seven-year-old, inland home with one-half acre of landscape (22,650 square feet) of which 12,600 square feet (56%) is turfgrass

The Problems: High water bills, poor turf appearance and consistent turf "hot spots".

The Solutions:
- The landscape contractor and local water agency developed an appropriate water budget for the site
- An audit of the irrigation system was performed to determine inefficiencies and system needs
- The irrigation system was adjusted and upgraded as recommended by the audit
- An ET water budget irrigation schedule was implemented
- The landscape water efficiency effort, including site audit and system upgrades, cost the homeowner $1,500.

The Results: Water use at the home was reduced 30%, saving 430,000 gallons of water in one year. Turf appearance improved and "hot spots" were eliminated.

The Winners: The homeowner saved enough water to pay for the landscape audit and upgrades in the first year. The landscape appearance and quality, especially the turf, improved. The landscape contractor performed extra or "new" work driven by the customer need to meet local water budget goals and reduce water bills.

Case Study No. 2

A 30 year old, 3,000 square foot home garden

This traditional garden consisted of the common design of the time, a large expanse of cool season lawn, foundation shrubs against the house and the occasional tree planted in the turf. The garden plants have varied over the years as the owners tastes and budgets allowed. The original design was neat and attractive, but lacked color or special interest that would set this home apart from any others. Increasingly higher amounts of water, fertilizer and labor were being used to maintain the garden.

The Problem: The homeowners wanted less garden maintenance, more color, lower water bills, environmental sensitivity and a more interesting appearance for enhancing the property value for future sale.

The Solution:
- **Planning:** The landscape contractor listened to the customer needs and desires, and helped develop a phased plan of garden changes. The plan recognized the site microclimates, areas of high water use and labor costs, and set priorities for retrofitting irrigation and using new plant materials.
- **Installation:** The specific work included soil testing, plant removal, soil amending, increasing perennial beds and fruit tree plantings, using drip irrigation in all shrub and tree areas and mulching all non-turf areas on a regular basis.
- **Maintenance:** Included using a soil probe to test for moisture before irrigating, using fertilizers only as soil tests suggested, using slow release fertilizer for the turf in warm months with iron to slow growth and maintain deep green color; less time was spent pruning and mowing

and more time was spent keeping the irrigation system operating efficiently and keeping mulch built up.

The Results: The home garden saves 40,000 gallons of water per year; the addition of perennials adds seasonal color and attracts wildlife; new shade trees cool the hot southwest side of the house and reduces energy bills; flowers and fruit are now products of the garden; curb appeal is high (cars slow to look at the garden as they drive by).

The Winners: The homeowner saves money on water and utility bills, gets a more colorful and contemporary landscape. The added pleasure and use of the garden increases the value of the garden for the owners as well as for the future resale value.

The landscape contractor assisted the homeowner with bringing their needs and desires to life; gains "new" retrofit work; provides higher value maintenance services and gains an attractive "model" for marketing home garden upgrades and resource efficient maintenance practices to future customers.

Case Study No. 3

Using advanced cultural practices to maintain the home garden

The Problem: An eight year old home with 2,000 s.f. of landscape needed to reduce water to meet local water budget allocations, but had no budget for significant irrigation or plant material changes.

The Goal: Meet water budgets with cultural and maintenance practices only.

The Solution:
- The contractor used a soil probe to monitor soil moisture before irrigating
- The local newspaper's weekly ET information was tracked to "check" irrigation water replacement needs
- Irrigation heads were adjusted for clearance over turf
- All heads were straightened and cleaned to maximize uniformity
- Heads were consistently adjusted to eliminate overspray
- Pressure was checked and pressure regulating devices were used to reduce misting (paid for by the overall savings in water bills)
- Turf was mowed with a mulching mower (mulched clippings help retain moisture and add slow release nutrients)
- Turf fertilization was changed from high nitrogen to iron-based balanced fertilizer (reducing growth rate and need for excess water while maintaining deep green color)
- Irrigation run-off time was determined to set the limits of irrigation run-times
- All shrub beds were mulched and watered one-half as much as the turf (checked by using a soil probe)

Who is responsible for high water bills from this inefficient irrigation system? The homeowner and the landscaper. Solution: add pressure regulation, adjust heads.

The Results: The home garden meets the local water budget, saving 75,000 gallons per year; the landscape health improves (no chlorosis, deeper rooted turf, more shrub flowering); less green waste produced.

The Winners: The homeowners reduce water bills and improve the health of the garden at no additional cost. The landscape contractor meets the challenge of reducing site water use without any extra cost or plant changes. The savings from reduced fertilization, reduced dump fees and less weeding time covers the cost of more advanced cultural practices. The landscaper is seen as a more valued partner in meeting the customer's needs.

CHAPTER 4
"Change" in the Landscape
This chapter describes attitudes that companies can build to more effectively market efficiency as a "new" business opportunity.

The previous case studies provide real world examples of what can happen when public agencies initiate water budget and water conservation programs in their areas. For landscape contractors, there is the potential to partner with customers and agencies to solve costly problems found in landscapes. Of course, there is also the option to try to hold on to old maintenance habits, resist change and ignore the genuine public need to use water and resources wisely.

The real change taking place is in the knowledge and attitude that contractors take to their sites. Seeing is believing, and contractors that practice effective water management see that water efficiency and water budgets do not destroy sites they manage. The belief in the credibility of the water budget science developed by university research programs, and the knowledge of real plant water needs is the important first step in gaining landscape water efficiency. It has become evident that the real change that is needed is not necessarily to replace high water use plants with lower water use plants, or to retrofit spray irrigation systems to drip systems, but to change the attitude of maintenance company owners and employees. Water efficiency makes sense today, tomorrow and in the future for green industry professionals. Understanding the issues and building the knowledge of how to care for a site in the most efficient way will help to make the green industry leaders in dealing with California water limitations.

The use of drip irrigation and mulch in parking lot and street applications

Integrating New Attitudes and Practices

The reality is that all water users, including landscapes, need to be water efficient in California. It is an essential belief for changing and potentially expanding business opportunity. The attitude within a company that resource efficient landscaping is the "right thing to do" environmentally, economically and competitively, is important when trying to integrate new approaches into company practices. Customers respond when site upgrades make economic sense and eliminate costly problems.

The first step is to find out the facts about your local area and your sites. Start by contacting the local Cooperative Extension office for weather, soil and plant data. Find out where you can get local ET weather data and how you can access that data every day (for example, weather data is available on the Internet). Look for educational opportunities for employees. Contact the local water agencies to learn about their water pricing and conservation programs.

Increased training and education are key to contractor success.

Know how much water a site uses.

With this information, evaluate how work is performed, on a site-by-site basis. How is irrigation scheduled and how often is it changed? Does it match the changes in weather? What is the local ET. How wet (or dry) is the soil? With this type of information, the landscape contractor can begin to formulate a plan of how to increase profits through increased labor efficiency, water efficiency and improved customer service for every contract site. Landscape contractors that apply resource efficient techniques on their sites save valuable labor time, save resources, can increase profits and improve the appearance of the landscape. Customers see a consistently attractive landscape with less problems.

Most importantly, find out everything you can regarding your sites. That information includes:

Site Information:

- Site water use history
- Landscape square footage (by meter)
- Irrigation equipment inventory and condition
- Site hydrozone water requirements (site map of irrigation stations and plants)
- Crop coefficient (Kc) or plant factor (water need) information on the plants at the site
- Local ETo (reference evapotranspiration) on a weekly basis
- Formulas (or software) for turning weather (ET) data into irrigation schedules
- Local water prices, billing information and conservation programs
- Irrigation system efficiency level
- Soil type, soil nutrient levels and water infiltration ability
- Take consistent soil probe samples to monitor turf root depth and soil moisture
- Listing of any site problems (hardscape damages, signs of water overspray or runoff, turf quality, green waste generation, fertilizing schedule, etc.)
- Site goals from the customer standpoint
- Site goals from the contractor standpoint
- Site budget

Other Important Site Numbers to Know:

- The cost to your customer for site maintenance (overall and itemized)
- The hidden costs of the site (i.e., street/paving erosion, fence damages, hardscape damages, root damages, over-water use cost, etc.)
- The cost to upgrade the site (irrigation system and/or plant materials)
- Customer pay-back time (total upgrade cost / yearly savings)

Contact the California Irrigation Management Information System (CIMIS) on the Internet: www.ceresgroup.com

Specific site knowledge enables you to use water and resource efficiency to work for you and your business.

Selling the Water Efficient Landscape

It's in the numbers that will convince customers to use your services and fund water and resource efficiency upgrades you recommend for a site. What numbers are we talking about and where do you find them? Every site is unique and will have its own set of numbers to gather.

Here is an example of how numbers can illustrate opportunities for a green industry company and help solve a customer problem. A homeowner association replaced eight-year-old wood fencing due to serious water damages. The cost was $550,000 for the fence replacement throughout the entire complex. Two months after the new fence was installed, water over-spray was beginning to discolor and destroy the second fence system. The

landscape contractor, armed with a new attitude and numbers, presented the association with a plan to retrofit and upgrade the entire landscape, changing the original plant and irrigation design to eliminate overspray problems causing the fence damage. The contractor showed that they could not only eliminate fence water damages, but street and parking lot paving erosion from water run-off. Water bills were also estimated to be reduced by at least 35%. The cost for a total landscape renovation was estimated to be $150,000, or 73% less expense than to replace the fencing ($550,000 plus inflation) again in eight years. The decision was made easy for the association by the landscaper.

Each site will be different, with a variety of slope, irrigation, tree, hardscape, plant material, age, soil, green waste, root, color, and/or budget problems. With experience, you will find opportunities for efficiency and marketing to take from site to site. Remember, you the maintenance contractor did not design the site landscape. But you, the landscape contractor, are the only one capable of remedying site problems and maintaining site value for the customer. Get to know the numbers for each site you manage.

(Below) New streetscape with sub-surface irrigation.
(Bottom and below, next page) Streetscape before; and after, with 50 percent less water and reduced paving damages.

More "New" Business for the Green Industry

New business for landscape contractors traditionally comes from the development of new homes and businesses with more landscape acreage installed. With the California population estimated to increase by 15 million people by the year 2020, there will be significant "new" business to meet demand. However, the recession of the early 1990's showed that counting on new development for increasing production can be a precarious business approach. Drought also slows or stops "new" landscape installations.

As population grows and water supplies are stretched, new development may be contingent upon **if** there is enough water available to meet existing and new urban demands. Currently 40%–70% of home water use goes to landscapes, depending on the local climate. **Making existing landscapes as water and resource efficient as possible is the best way the green industry can contribute to helping urban water supplies meet <u>new</u> development demands.** There is an estimated 1.0 to 1.5 million acres of existing landscaping in the state. Over the next 20 years, with a 48 % increase in population expected, some

500,00 to 750,000 acres of **new** landscape could be in demand by the public. The opportunities for green industry solutions for water efficiency are everywhere. In new landscapes with new designs, with new irrigation systems and new plant materials that increase water efficiency. But, more importantly, in **existing** landscapes that need new designs, upgraded irrigation systems, new plant materials and advanced maintenance practices to achieve water efficiency. Making existing landscapes water efficient represents a significant opportunity for the green industry to add "new" business. Retrofitting existing landscapes to be water efficient is a relatively untapped market for green industry businesses. And, improving a landscapes water efficiency will help make water available for new development. Practice water efficiency on every site for every customer, new or old.

Create marketing tools and materials that highlight your company's abilities. Market your services that protect and enhance the customers property values. Don't just talk about a healthy landscape, create efficient and cost-effective landscapes that use actual site numbers that show the results you can bring to your current and prospective customers.

Customer Service

Read any book on business success and it will tell you that what makes the difference between success and failure is QUALITY CUSTOMER SERVICE. Interviews for this handbook with landowners, developers, city staff, homeowner associations, and landscape professionals revealed that the customer perception of service provided by landscape contractors is considered low. Customers do not understand the scope of managing the dynamic changes presented by "nature" in the landscape. Customers do have problems in their landscapes. Those problems can be expensive and a challenge to correct. The one business that can educate, unravel and solve the customer's landscape problems is the landscape contractor. That fact alone should lead to higher valued contracts and greater confidence in the industry.

Example Marketing Tools:

- Water use histories of your sites compared to weather and water budgets
- Cost savings you have accomplished for customers in graphic form
- Photos of water efficient sites
- Before and after photos of cost-effective retrofits
- User friendly weekly/monthly irrigation scheduling reports
- Step by step water management program/services your company offers

Practice high quality customer service. Do that by using site specific numbers on the costs to maintain a high quality landscape. Point out the hidden costs of a poorly maintained landscape and the benefits of a top quality maintenance program for the customer. Without quality customer service, the public develops a perception of landscape maintenance that undervalues the important services offered by the landscape professional.

When presented with real numbers and the vision of an upgraded, efficient and attractive asset (the landscape), customers will make the cost effective choice. It is up to the contractor to make that case for the customer. Higher quality service **does** pay for itself for the customer. Show the customer how...

A case in point is a homeowner association with 38 acres of landscape, 25 years old with large slopes, thousands of trees, meandering turf greenbelts and foundation plants up to the homes. The landscape contractor is under pressure from the association board because water costs and the incidence of irrigation failures and fixes have continued to rise. Wood fences and street paving is consistently damaged by water. The turf, shrubs and groundcover plantings were not meeting the visual expectations of the association.

How does the contractor meet the customer expectations, reduce rising costs, upgrade the landscape appearance and retain the site contract?

- **Step 1** – Analyze the site costs for water, repairs of the irrigation equipment, upgrades of old, inefficient heads and hidden costs.

- **Step 2** – Listen to the customer's desires and educate the customer on the "real" reasons behind the failing landscape (i.e, design, age, vandalism, etc.). *Note: It is important that the real site problems don't become excuses by the contractor. Many problems are caused by external forces over which the contractor has no control. The contractor should take responsibility for the role maintenance has in causing problems and help the customer understand what it takes to eliminate them. Often, the cost to supply a service, say water management, is less than the cost of excess water use to the customer.*

- **Step 3** – Analyze the contract. Is it specific as to the customer's desires and does it provide enough time to perform high quality service for the customer? *(Don't continue to work sites that cost you money and tarnish your reputation.)*

- **Step 4** – Come armed with facts. Don't go to meetings with customers unprepared or defensive. Know what the water use of the site is and what the local ET says it should be. The difference in those two numbers is money that can be saved for the customer. Bring solutions for getting water spray off of fences and streets and know how much it will cost. Find out what the hidden costs are for hardscape damages, fences, street paving, etc. As money is always an issue for customers, devise a phased retrofit plan of attack for the customer, and remember that every efficiency upgrade should immediately begin to save either water or labor time or both. That translates into better customer service, better customer relations, higher profits and a more successful site. *(It may be helpful at this point to bring in an outside horticulture consultant to act as a facilitator between the contractor and the customer.)*

What happened on the 38 acre homeowner association site? The landscape contractor enlisted the help of an outside horticultural consultant to meet the customer and walk the site. The outside consultant was needed to play the part of a facilitator to assist with the site assessment, educating the customer for the site potential and estimates of savings and help develop a site master plan. The efforts included:

- Educating the customer regarding opportunities for savings
- Helping the customer identify the goals for the site
- Making the customer's goals the goals of the contractor
- Helping the customer understand the need to implement

Site retrofit that solved customer problems of high water bills, tree root surfacing, water damage to fences, and lack of color.

(Top right) Before— uninspiring landscape. (Immediate right) Turf sculpting around trees, old shrubs removed. (Far right) New plant placement with drip irrigation.

the solutions to the site problems (as opposed to the crisis management approach of fixing the symptoms instead of curing the problem)

● Suggesting substantial changes for the long-term landscape health, not band-aid fixes. This was done by using the site "numbers" to show the cost effectiveness of "doing it right" versus "doing it quick and cheap".

Did the effort work in terms of upgrading the landscape and keeping the contractor on the site? Yes. The association agreed to a master plan that detailed the types of irrigation system upgrades to perform, what plant material changes to make to increase color and reduce maintenance time, what areas to treat as priorities and how to phase the implementation of the upgrades to accommodate the association budget. The contractor not only kept the job but also became a partner with the customer to remedy site problems. The landscape contract was revised to detail the highest valued work and pay the contractor for more sophisticated work.

(Top) Before—the uninspiring, colorless landscape.
(Above) Retrofit, upgraded landscape cut water bills by 50%, cut maintenance cost 20 percent, improved property value, solved a variety of customer problems

Once the customer understood the high and never ending costs for band-aid fixes to an old and poorly designed site versus the costs for long-term solutions, the relationship and efforts between the contractor and customer changed for the better. A new level of customer service began with understanding the site numbers and looking for solutions that would be cost effective for the customer. With this type of approach, contractors can perform more retrofit work (new business), gain higher customer acceptance (raise industry standards) and increase profits.

This example, and previous case studies, show that analyzing site problems, looking for cost saving opportunities and listening to the customer needs translate into higher quality customer service. Customer service pays. Every landscape customer in California will have the need to be water efficient in the coming years. That need will grow as population increases. The green industry, and particularly the landscape contractor, has the unique position to offer solutions to each and every customer. Those solutions should be viewed as customer service, not just water management, or grass-cycling, or mulching, or matching irrigation heads. Every landscape customer will need higher quality, integrated landscape services. That need, like the need for water, will never go away.

CHAPTER 5
Optimizing Landscape Water Efficiency

This chapter describes more specific horticultural information contractors can consider to help make a site water and resource efficient. The techniques and practices are intended to supply the contractor with more site knowledge, produce a healthier landscape, prevent problems before they occur and help save valuable labor time. *Recommendations for your specific sites may vary due to local soil, weather, landscape design, water prices, etc.*

Use this information in combination with other horticultural research to determine the best care for your landscape.

This chapter is:

❧ A guide to management techniques th can save contractor's time and save make) money
❧ Designed to help produce healthier a more attractive landscapes with le resources
❧ Intended to help contractors identify ways to improve site profits, contract specifications and customer service

I. Cultural Practices: It All Starts With the Soil

"There are conditions of urban soils that present the most difficult problems to landscape professionals."

The Landscape Below Ground

The Best Maintenance Practices (BMPs) for a Water and Resource Efficient Landscape are identified as:

I.   Sound Cultural Practices
II. Preventive Irrigation Maintenance
III. Water Budget Irrigation Scheduling

Every discussion of how to achieve a healthy, attractive and efficient landscape starts below ground level with the soil. Every water and resource efficient landscape needs the site's soil to provide essential elements for plants to be successful. The water and resource efficient landscape is the site that receives only the amount of water plants need for healthy growth, receives fertilizer only when it is lacking, and restores a more natural balance by recycling organic material into the soil.

Every commercial landscape and home garden, it seems, has its own set of soil conditions that make site management a challenge. The complaints most often heard are: "hardpan," "run-off," "compaction," "nutrient deficiency," "yellow leaves," "surface roots," and on and on. Stop complaining. Get to know and understand the site's soil. Start with a soil test.

Test the Soil

Typical landscape contracts call for regular fertilizer applications regardless of the needs of the soil. The regular <u>over</u> application of fertilizer, particularly nitrogen, starts a cycle of more rapid growth, higher water use and increased labor requirements for the contractor. Do the plants and soil really need the fertilization as specified by most contracts? A field soil test, prior to fertilizer applications, will tell the site manager if nutrients are really needed. A laboratory soils test is appropriate to help analyze for more complex site problems. A field soils test or lab test is inexpensive when compared to the purchase and application of fertilizers. Soil testing is also very effective when compared to the labor time and dump fees associated with increased plant growth resulting from excessive fertilizers.

One city has written the use of soil testing <u>before</u> applying fertilizers into landscape maintenance contracts. The result has been a reduction of fertilizer applications from five times per year to two. The savings to the city comes in the form of lower fertilizer costs, reduced water need (from excessive growth) by the plants and reduced green waste production. With the aid of a soil test,

contractors gain ongoing knowledge of the site, reduce labor time for unnecessary work, avoid overstimulating plant growth, reduce dump fees and save wear on machinery and vehicles.

Use a soil test to verify the need and justify the cost of the time and labor it takes to apply fertilizer to the landscape. This sophistication and the professionalism, on the part of the landscape contractor, improves the image of the company in the eyes of the customer. Performing a soil test and using the results shows the client that you are spending their money wisely.

What to Order in a Basic Soil Test:

A field soil test should look for nitrogen and pH. With a basic laboratory soil test, the following elements should be examined: nitrogen, phosphorus, potassium, calcium, magnesium, salts (sodium, SAR) & pH

A typical laboratory soils test as described above may cost approximately $25.

Properties of Soils:

Sandy Soil – fast drainage, low nutrient holding capacity, difficult to compact, allows deep root growth, fast water penetration rate, low water holding capacity

Loam Soil – good nutrient holding capacity, good structure, good drainage, good water infiltration rate, moderate to good water holding capacity

Clay Soil – high nutrient holding capacity, little pore space for roots (especially when wet), slow water infiltration rate, high compaction potential, high water holding capacity

What Plants Need From Soil:

- Soil with adequate pore space
- Deep, penetrable soil profile
- Good soil structure with uniform texture throughout the soil profile
- Moderate water holding capacity
- Adequate drainage
- pH in an acceptable range

Using a Soil Probe

Getting to know the site's soil requires the use of a test to measure chemical and fertility levels. A soil probe is a field tool that offers fast and easy access to knowing the soils moisture content, plant root depth and health (especially in turf), the presence of hardpan layering and depth of water penetration in relation to the plant root zone. The use of a soil probe provides direct information a supervisor, irrigator and field hand need to help make management decisions that produce a water efficient landscape.

Make a soil probe standard equipment and require all site supervisors and irrigators to use probes daily. Soil probes are the quickest and least expensive way to monitor what is happening below ground. The combination of periodic soil testing and the use of a soil probe increases the knowledge the contractor has about the site and how to best manage the soil to insure the plant roots have the environment they need to be healthy.

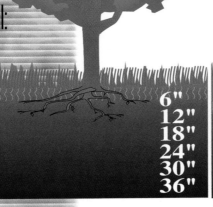

Urban Soil

Slow water infiltration; compaction; limited air spaces; shallow roots; water saturation from poor drainage

Good Soil

Air spaces; bacterial action; some moisture deep into the soil profile; ability to drain excess water

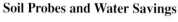

Soil Probes and Water Savings

Home sites in Orange County were studied to see if use of a soil probe saved landscape water. The study was conducted during the three highest irrigation months, July, August and September. The monthly water use of the test homes was averaged over the last 5 years and compared to the 3 test months of 1997. A group of neighboring homes water use, without the benefit of soil probes, was evaluated for the same period as a control group. The water use was weather normalized.

The study results showed that during July, August and September of 1997, water use at the soil probe test homes decreased 14.7%. The water use at the control homes (no soil probes) increased 9.2%. The difference between homes using soil probes versus homes not using soil probes was 23.9% in water use.

The findings of the study established that the use of soil probes, before irrigating, to monitor soil moisture can save significant water in the landscape. (See appendix II for soil probe references.)

Water Infiltration and Penetration

The soils of urban landscapes are typically compacted through the construction process, from traffic and use. Water, where the infiltration rate is slow, has a difficult time penetrating compacted soils. Much of the water applied beyond the soils infiltration rate becomes wasted water run-off. Customers literally pay for water running down the street. Urban soils, with slow water infiltration rates, limited water penetration ability, that receive under or over-watering often have shallow and surface rooting plants.

How do you determine if water penetration is a problem? The common practice is to dig a hole, fill it with water and wait to see how long it takes to soak into the ground. The slower the water soaks into the ground, the more difficult that soil is to irrigate and move water down into the root zone. Another method is to use a soil probe. First, if you can't drive the probe into the soil, chances are that water and plant roots are also not able to penetrate the soil. If the probe stops a few inches below the surface, it's another sign that water and roots will also have difficulty going deeper than a few inches. If the probe goes into the ground easily and the soil core is seen to be fully wet, the soil should be allowed to dry (50% depletion rate is generally recommended) before irrigating again. At the saturation point, additional water becomes run-off or moisture below the root zone and is no value to the landscape and costly to the customer. Use consistent site monitoring with a hand soil probe to know when it is time to turn the water on or off.

Root Depth

The depth of plant roots in the soil is a function of the soil texture, whether sand, silt or clay, the pore space available, plant genetics and the water penetration into the soil. If water can penetrate deeply and adequate air is

What Urban Soils Often Provide:

- Compaction with limited air space for roots
- Nutrient imbalances (salts, low iron, boron)
- Low or no organic material
- Low micro-bacterial activity
- Layers of different soil textures and/or hardpan (limiting the movement of water)
- Slow water infiltration
- Poor drainage

The CLCA Landscape Standards Committee

recommends the use of soil probes to test for subsoil moisture for trees, shrubs and groundcovers on a bimonthly schedule. Soil probes should be used on a regular basis to "evaluate actual soil moisture levels and irrigation schedules."

Common Site/Soil Problems:

- Contractors inherit sites with poor soils, inefficient irrigation systems and difficult hydrozones
- Typical maintenance habits, such as high water applications and excessive fertilization contribute to common landscape problems
- Maintenance contracts that do not encourage resource efficient practices
- Customers consistently wanting to cut back on landscape maintenance contracts/ expenditures (perception of landscape as a low value asset)

The Solutions:

Work with the customer on a site program that includes:

- Analyze maintenance actions for it's time, cost and landscape success (plant health and attractiveness)
- Add up the costs of resources used for a site (water and fertilizer, etc.)
- List the complaints associated with the site landscape and time, money and resources spent to correct the problems
- Compare the above with using a preventative maintenance, resource efficient customer service approach

present, roots can follow. By growing deeper, roots fill a greater soil area which increases the potential reservoir of water available to the plants. Root depth then becomes a mechanism that helps make plants healthier and the landscape more water efficient. The value of building deep roots is illustrated in the following example:

A high-tech commercial business development consists of large expanses of turf (95% of the site acreage) and evergreen trees, intended to present an attractive and sought-after location for businesses. The Tall Fescue landscape was well designed, the top few inches of soil amended and had state-of-the art irrigation equipment of the late 1980's. The predominant soil of the area is clay. By all indications, the 128 acres of business complex landscapes should have been performing well and be attractive within a 100% ET water budget.

Organic material for turf aeration

Within a few years of installation, most of the site was receiving 50%-100% more water than University of California turf research suggests should be applied. At the same time the turf showed consistent summer "hot spots," stress or burn patterns.

The turf stress occurred even with the high amounts of irrigation. The timing could not have been worse. The area was in the middle of an extended drought (1987-93). The state's economic recession was firmly in place and landscape contracts were under pressure to be reduced. High water bills were the cause of great stress for the customer and the contractor. The contractor was subject to significant criticism for high water bills and poor turf appearance from the developer and property manager.

What was happening? At the first signs of turf stress, the contractor turned up the water. When the weather continued to be hot and the turf continued to burn, increasing the water was the only maintenance response. The common practice of applying monthly, high nitrogen fertilization continued (under the premise that more fertilizer and more water would make the problem go away). Nothing short of flood irrigation worked. Some turf areas actually received 200 inches of water in a climate area that called for 48 inches annually.

Raising irrigation heads to clear fast-growing turf

Soil probe checking for root and moisture depth

The cost of the water drove the land owner, water district and a landscape consultant to take a systematic look at how best to manage this site in a cost effective and attractive way. The findings were:

- Clay soils were saturated with water
- Compaction and/or lack of soil oxygen was increased by over watering
- Nitrogen fertilizers contributed to fast top growth but little root development
- Tall Fescue turf had 1.5"-2.0" deep roots
- The top 2" of soil would dry out in a single hot summer day, causing consistent turf stress, even with a previous night's irrigation
- Tree roots surfaced due to compaction
- Turf, due to high fertilization and water, would grow rapidly, blocking spray heads
- Irrigation heads had sunk in the wet soil, causing blockage of spray heads
- Irrigation heads were not straight or well maintained
- Irrigation heads were clogged
- Water run-off occurred within 2 minutes of irrigation run-times
- Irrigation cycles were set for 7-10 minutes

By analyzing the site, from the soil and root zone, to the weekly cultural practices, the "numbers" presented a clear picture of the site challenge. A new set of maintenance guidelines needed to be developed. The sites' water efficient turf maintenance program emerged to include the following:

- Aerate 3 times per year (early spring, late spring, early fall) to open up compacted soils for increasing turf root depth
- Add organic top dressing immediately after every aeration to increase biological activity in the soil
- Eliminate high doses of nitrogen fertilizer and replace it with a slow release balanced fertilizer with iron (to maintain deep green turf color)
- Use of mulching mowers and grasscycling to moderate turf water and nutrient needs
- Apply specific aeration and top dressing to turf "hot spots" to allow for greater water penetration
- Apply a preventative irrigation maintenance program (routinely checking and adjusting low, blocked or clogged heads)
- Irrigation to move water deep into the soil, then let the soil dry to 50% field capacity moisture level to allow oxygen exchange
- Irrigation as per weather (ET) changes, including reading meters weekly, using irrigation scheduling software and soil probing to check moisture and turf rooting
- Irrigation with short run times of 2-3 minutes per cycle to minimize water run-off

The result, over the 128 acre business park, is a healthier, more attractive landscape that meets water budgets. Turf roots have grown to a depth of 5-6". Turf is irrigated 50% less during summer and the overall water use is down 56% when compared to past years. The presence of turf stress or "hot spots" has been significantly reduced. All these improvements came about because of attention paid to the three "best maintenance practices" for a water efficient landscape; (1) Sound cultural practices, (2) Preventive irrigation system maintenance, and (3) Scheduling irrigation as per ET. Water bills were reduced 75% while visual appearance, and turf health, were greatly improved. The customer has the valuable marketing asset (the landscape) they desire, maintained with better appearance at a lower cost.

The message from this example is clear. Manage the soils with proper cultural practices, use the right amount of water and do not cut corners on preventive maintenance. The landscape, in turn, will be water efficient, cost effective and more attractive. For the contractor and the customer, these practices amount to nothing more than quality customer service.

Example Site Water Costs/Reduction Through the Program Above				
1992	1993	1994	1995	1996
$523,275	$244,581	$240,999	$134,036	$133,313

1996 had a higher ET than any other year shown with average rainfall, yet achieved the lowest water bills during the period.

Aeration – Making Turf More Water Efficient

Soils under turf are often compacted soils. Compaction limits root growth and depth. For turf with 2" deep roots, increasing the root area 1" increases the area from which turf can pull water by 33%. Aeration of the soil, at the right time of year, provides a more favorable environment for deeper root growth.

Aerate soils when the turf roots are most actively growing. The first aeration of the year should be started as soon as the rain and temperature allow. In early spring, turf roots are starting up growth as the soil temperature warms. Late spring or early summer is the next aeration opportunity. At those times, turf roots are still expanding. Cool season grasses slow or stop root growth expansion during the hot summer months and aeration has little positive impact. Aerate again in late September or early October to coincide with cool season turf root activity. Warm season grasses may

Aeration to help build deeper turf roots

need only a single aeration since they have a shorter growing season and more vigorous roots. (However, nitrogen applications can help extend the green color of warm season grass into the late fall.)

Mulch, Mulch and More Mulch

One of the surest ways to save water in the landscape is to use mulch. The consistent use of organic mulch creates an interface with soil that shields the soil surface from the sun that bakes and hardens the top of the soil. By covering the soil surface, mulch helps water penetration into the soil. The water saving function of mulch is that it insulates the soil to reduce evaporation. Mulch also reduces weed growth in planter areas. The use of mulch can more than off-set the labor cost of weeding. Find a reliable source of shredded, thoroughly composted, organic mulch and use it for every tree, shrub and ground cover area in every landscape, including slopes. (Note: keep mulch away from the base of plants to avoid trunk rot potential.)

Grasscycling: Mulch for the Turf

Grasscycling simply creates mulch for turf areas. Research has shown that grasscycling, the practice of using mulching mowers and leaving the grass clippings in the turf, reduces evaporation and returns nitrogen to the soil.

Mulch that is shredded does stay in place on hillsides. CalTrans shown mulching miles of freeway landscapes.

- Stockpile the site's topsoil for use after construction is completed
- Generally, plant trees and shrubs in the native soil. Roots will extend well beyond the original planting hole. Since soil cannot be uniformly amended throughout the area that will eventually be filled by the roots of the trees and shrubs, save time and money by putting trees and shrubs directly into well tilled native soil.
- Apply mulch to a 2-4' layer on the soil surface around trees, shrubs and ground covers. Keep mulch a few inches away from the base of plants to reduce the potential of trunk and root rots.
- Completely mix in amendment in turf and ground cover planting areas as deep as possible

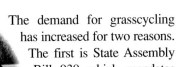

(Left) Mulch covers drip irrigation. (Above) Mulch gives more attractive appearance than barren soil.

Problem:

- Typical landscape maintenance contracts specify monthly or bimonthly fertilization for turf. The high application of nitrogen invites a cycle of higher water use, more labor and more fertilizer, making the site water and resource intensive (i.e., costly).

Solution:

- Rewrite contracts to include higher quality services, i.e. soil testing, aeration, dethatching and mulching
- Use soil tests to determine the nutrient needs of the site before fertilizing
- Use slow-release fertilizers and mulching mowers to help produce "green" grass without excessive growth

The demand for grasscycling has increased for two reasons. The first is State Assembly Bill 939 which mandates that the waste stream going to landfills must be cut by 50% by the year 2000. Generally, 25%-30% of all landfill material is green waste. This material must be diverted away from landfills by law.

The second reason to use grasscycling is the ability to reduce evaporation from lawns and gain "free" nitrogen from the microbiotic breakdown of the clippings. By using a mulching mower, the grass clippings are ground into a fine material that does not lay on the surface of the grass, but drops down among the grass leaves. (The fallen clippings form a kind of mulch above the grass stems and act as an insulation to reduce evaporation.) As the clippings break down they give off moisture, cooling the grass leaves, and release nitrogen for plant uptake.

Contrary to conventional wisdom, mulched grass clippings **do not** cause thatch build-up in turf. Thatch is caused by a build-up of plant shoots, stems and rhizomes. Mulched grass clippings break down fast and do not build thatch in turf. Use grasscycling as a means of saving labor while improving the quality of turf at the same time. (For more information on grasscycling, contact your local Cooperative Extension office. See Appendix V.)

II. Preventive Irrigation Maintenance Program

Water efficiency cannot be achieved by simply turning the water down (not if you want to keep the landscape attractive and keep the job). An inventory and prioritized action item list of irrigation system repairs and upgrades is needed and the action items must be implemented. Only then can water efficiency begin.

To be water efficient, month by month, the same action item list should be used as part of a preventive maintenance program for every site. Taking care of a site's irrigation system makes good business sense. It is a prime component of the customer's landscape asset. A preventative maintenance program will save time compared to a crisis management approach that takes over when "hot spots" occur, or when irrigation equipment fails and water bills go sky high. Plan ahead and look for problems before they happen. Check for the following problems:

(Above) Pop-up spray head that does not reach above the grass. (Right) All heads were repaired or replaced with higher pop-ups. This retrofit costs less than over-watering.

- Sprinkler heads spaced too far apart
- Mismatched heads
- System distribution and uniformity
- System operating pressure and pressure regulation needs
- Sprinkler throw and arc
- Height of heads in relation to turf and other plants
- Tilting heads
- Clogged heads
- Sunken heads
- Low head drainage and the need for check valves

All of these items will affect water application, system uniformity and efficiency. These same items affect plant health, appearance and customer satisfaction. Avoid customer complaints and dissatisfaction by practicing consistent preventive maintenance and fixing problems before they cost you the contract.

All heads have "sunk" and/or are low due to thatch build-up.

III. Water Budget Irrigation Scheduling:

"Plants need the right amount of water at the right time and at the right place."

Gardening for Dummies

How Much Water Do Plants Need?

Different plant species need different amounts of water. No one gets it right all the time. How do you know how much water to apply to a landscape?

Use a soil probe to "see and feel" the moisture level in the soil and in the plant root zone

Monitor the weather (ET) and keep a weekly chart

Track the amount of water being applied to the site and compare the actual use with the local ET

Apply only the water lost by the plants to evapotranspiration (see the estimated water need of plants in Appendix V, WUCOLS)

Plants need water based on (1) their unique physiological requirements, (2) root volume depth and mass, (3) in relation to local environmental factors, such as light, temperature, wind and humidity. More roots at a deeper level enable plants to pull water from a larger soil area, increasing plant health, efficiency and even drought tolerance. A plants physiology and water use capabilities are referred to as their crop coefficient (Kc) or plant factor. For a listing of common landscape plants and their estimated water requirements, see Appendix V.

California Irrigation Management Information System (CIMIS) weather station measuring daily ETo.

Generally, plants can be classified in simple ranges of low, medium and high water users. Plant water need varies, even among species from the same genus. Cool season fescue grass represents the reference (ETo) for ornamental landscape plants. CIMIS weather stations, and other private manufacturer systems, measure the water transpired/evaporated by cool season fescue grass. The measurement refers to its maximum evapotranspiration rate, written as 100% or 1.0 of ET.

New plantings with smaller root mass at shallow soil depths may require more water and more frequent irrigations for establishment. Mature plants can perform at the lower end of the listed plant factor levels. Soil type and slopes have little impact on a plant's water need, though the site's

The Problems:

● The soil surface looks dry. Both the home gardener and the landscape professional react by turning up the water. But, does the plant really need more water?

Or:

● A watering schedule is programmed into a controller. This is done without evaluating the soil moisture and/or health of the plant materials. Water is applied to the landscape without knowing how much is really needed. The schedule remains unchanged for months or all year.

The Solution:

● Use a soil probe to determine the moisture content below the soil surface. It is a reliable way to tell if the soil is wet or dry (DO NOT rely on looking at the soil surface for soil moisture information)

● Observe the plants, feel for leaf turgidity, look at leaf color and wilting as signs of stress, etc.

● Find out how much water is being applied to the landscape (read the water meter weekly or after a typical stations run cycle; turn the ccfs into inches of water). Compare the actual use on the site to local weather (ET) in inches or ccfs. Turn the difference into a percentage and adjust the site controllers accordingly. A real site example is:

Site Area: 1 acre

Weekly ET: .84 inches/acre (30.5 ccfs for the week)

Actual Weeks Water Application: 1.15 inches (41.7 ccfs)

Water budget equation:

$$\frac{(30.5 \text{ ccf}) (.75 \text{ Kc}) (1 \text{ acre})}{(.80 \text{ IE})} = 28.6 \text{ ccf/week}$$

Actual Water Use: 9,800 gallons, or 31% overwatering for the week

(Below) University research plot determining plant water needs (Kc)

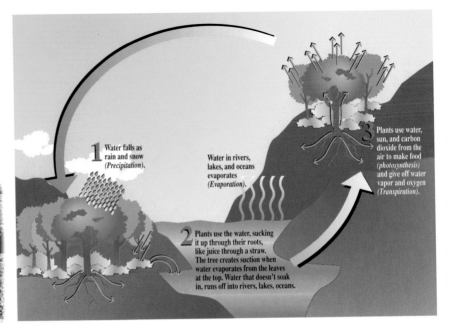

1 Water falls as rain and snow *(Precipitation).*

Water in rivers, lakes, and oceans evaporates *(Evaporation).*

2 Plants use the water, sucking it up through their roots, like juice through a straw. The tree creates suction when water evaporates from the leaves at the top. Water that doesn't soak in, runs off into rivers, lakes, oceans.

3 Plants use water, sun, and carbon dioxide from the air to make food *(photosynthesis)* and give off water vapor and oxygen *(Transpiration).*

Soil probes help water managers assess irrigation schedule impacts in the soil.

soil certainly impacts how easily water gets into the plant root zone and how long it remains in that zone.

Landscape contractors are constantly presented with site variables that complicate efficient water management. They include:

● Micro-climates of sun and shade

● Multiple species plantings (such as trees in turf)

● Heat islands (parking lots, streets, buildings, etc.)

● Poorly designed irrigation systems (systems not separated between micro-climates or turf and shrub areas, spacing, pressure and head blockage, etc.)

Among the best options for addressing such problems are consistent use of soil probes to monitor soil moisture and tracking the local ET and matching it to watering schedules. Keep the customer informed of the site problems. As water costs rise, contractors can develop cost/benefit analyses to show customers how much upgraded irrigation systems and/or plant material upgrades would cost in relation to continuing to pay existing expenses. If the savings justifies the costs, new business and a more water efficient landscape can be created by the contractor.

General Plant Factors (estimated water needs) Compared to Reference ET (100%)

● **Turf** – High/Medium High, Cool Season Turf – 80%-100% or (.8 - 1.0), Warm Season Turf – 60%-80% (.6 - .8)

● **Groundcovers** – Medium/Medium High, – 50% - 80% or (.5 - .8)

● **Shrubs** – Medium/Low, 50% or (.5)

● **Trees** – Medium/Low, 50% or (.5)

● **Natives** – Low, 50% or below (.5 and lower)

● **Annuals** – Medium/High, 60%-100% or (.6 - 1.0)

Source: U.C. Cooperative Extension

CIMIS–Current & Historical Weather Station Sites

Evapotranspiration (ET) is the combined process of evaporation from the soil and plant surfaces and transpiration of water through plant materials. Contact your local Cooperative Extension office or the Department of Water Resources (DWR) for local ET information.

Contact your local water district to obtain sources of weather information.

Stn #	Station Name	Nearby City	County	Start Date	End Date
90	Alturas	Alturas	Modoc	4/23/89	
125	Arvin-Edison	Arvin	Kern	3/22/95	
134	Barstow NE	Barstow	San Bernardino	1/8/97	
60	Barstow	Barstow	San Bernardino	11/20/86	2/20/92
35	Bishop	Bishop	Inyo	2/4/83	
54	Blackwells Corner	Blackwells Corner	Kern	10/19/86	
135	Blythe NE	Blythe	Riverside	1/16/97	
36	Blythe	Blythe	Riverside	3/13/83	8/12/88
47	Brentwood	Brentwood	Contra Costa	11/18/85	
73	Hollywood Hills	Burbank	Los Angeles	3/4/88	9/14/93
41	Calipatria/Mulberry	Calipatria	Imperial	7/17/83	
29	Cantua Creek	Cantua Creek	Fresno	1/2/83	7/23/85
19	Castroville	Castroville	Monterey	11/18/82	
118	Cathedral City	Cathedral City	Riverside	12/7/95	
12	Durham	Chico	Butte	10/19/82	
82	Claremont	Claremont	Los Angeles	4/13/89	
32	Colusa	Colusa	Colusa	1/13/83	
11	Bakersfield/Bonanza	Conner	Kern	9/29/82	4/17/86
20	Corcoran	Corcoran	Kings	11/22/82	4/9/86
123	Suisun Valley	Cordelia	Solano	8/18/94	
88	Cuyama	Cuyama	Santa Barbara	5/20/89	
110	Newberry Springs	Dagget	San Bernardino	2/21/92	12/27/96
6	Davis	Davis	Yolo	7/1/82	
121	Dixon	Dixon	Solano	9/20/94	
122	Hastings Tract	Dixon	Solano	3/28/95	
87	Meloland	El Centro	Imperial	12/12/89	
74	Escondido	Escondido	San Diego	4/26/88	
131	Fair Oaks	Fair Oaks	Sacramento	4/18/97	
124	Panoche	Firebaugh	Fresno	7/27/95	
7	Firebaugh/Telles	Firebaugh	Fresno	9/22/82	
2	FivePoints/ WSFS USDA	Five Points	Fresno	6/7/82	
100	Fremont	Fremont	Alameda	8/29/91	
1	Fresno/F.S.U. USDA	Fresno	Fresno	6/7/82	9/25/88
80	Fresno State	Fresno	Fresno	10/3/88	
108	Gerber Dryland	Gerber	Tehama	3/11/91	
8	Gerber	Gerber	Tehama	9/22/82	
43	McArthur	Glenburn	Shasta	10/31/83	
133	Glendale	Glendale	Los Angeles	8/7/96	
94	Goleta Foothills	Goleta	Santa Barbara	7/7/90	
53	Greenfield	Greenfield	Monterey	10/10/86	10/23/91
120	Guadalupe	Guadalupe	Santa Barbara	12/24/93	
76	Betteravia	Guadalupe	Santa Barbara	12/18/87	7/1/93
92	Kesterson	Gustine	Merced	10/13/89	
51	Healdsburg	Healdsburg	Sonoma	8/24/86	3/28/94
126	San Benito	Hollister	San Benito	6/9/94	
106	Sanel Valley	Hopland	Mendocino	2/1/91	
85	Hopland FS	Hopland	Mendocino	9/23/89	
75	Irvine	Irvine	Orange	10/7/87	
21	Kettleman	Kettleman City	Kings	11/19/82	
113	King City-Oasis Rd.	King City	Monterey	6/12/93	
23	King City	King City	Monterey	11/19/82	12/23/85
9	Lamont	LaMont	Kern	9/29/82	4/10/89
93	Lamont	Lamont	Kern	2/4/90	10/3/94
22	Caruthers	Laton	Kings	11/18/82	6/6/88
86	Lindcove	Lindcove	Tulare	5/31/89	
42	Lodi	Lodi	San Joaquin	10/16/83	
102	El Dorado	Long Beach	Los Angeles	10/24/90	
56	Los Banos	Los Banos	Merced	6/28/88	
26	Lost Hills	Lost Hills	Kern	11/29/82	8/13/86
46	MacDoel	MacDoel	Siskiyou	11/11/85	6/11/86
138	Famoso	Macfarland	Kern	4/9/97	
70	Manteca	Manteca	San Joaquin	11/12/87	
84	Browns Valley	Marysville	Yuba	4/13/89	
31	McFarland/ Kern Farms	McFarland	Kern	1/11/83	3/8/93
17	El Centro	Meloland	Imperial	11/8/82	5/27/87
40	Mendota/ MuriettaUSDA	Mendota	Fresno	6/14/83	4/15/92
10	Bakersfield/Greenlee	Mettler Station	Kern	10/1/82	4/16/86
71	Modesto	Modesto	Stanislaus	6/25/87	
109	Carneros	Napa	Napa	3/11/93	
77	Oakville	Napa	Napa	3/1/89	
30	Nicolaus	Nicolaus	Sutter	1/3/83	
128	Salton Sea East	Niland	Imperial	11/17/94	
63	Novato	Novato	Marin	7/1/86	3/5/97
136	Oasis	Oasis/Indio	Riverside	1/7/97	
49	Oceanside	Oceanside	San Diego	3/11/86	
14	Orland (inactive)	Orland	Glenn	10/30/82	4/21/87
61	Orland	Orland	Glenn	5/13/87	
129	Pajaro	Pajaro	Monterey	9/13/95	
55	Palm Desert	Palm Desert	Riverside	5/26/87	4/11/94
72	Palo Verde	Palo Verde	Imperial	9/8/87	
39	Parlier	Parlier	Fresno	5/23/83	
101	Piru	Piru	Ventura	8/27/91	
13	Camino	Placerville	El Dorado	10/19/82	
81	Shenandoah Valley	Plymouth	Amador	5/11/90	
78	Pomona	Pomona	Los Angeles	3/14/89	
97	Port Hueneme	Port Hueneme	Ventura	2/16/91	
98	Ramona	Ramona	San Diego	4/20/91	
34	Rancho California	Rancho California	Riverside	1/21/83	11/25/86
62	Temecula	Rancho California	Riverside	11/25/86	
25	Rancho Mirage	Rancho Mirage	Riverside	11/22/82	11/20/85
140	Twitchell Island	Rio Vista	Sacramento		
44	U.C. Riverside	Riverside	Riverside	6/2/85	
115	Gonzales	Salinas	Monterey	6/18/93	
116	Salinas North	Salinas	Monterey	6/18/93	
37	USDA Salinas	Salinas	Monterey	4/11/83	7/27/92
89	Salinas South	Salinas	Monterey	9/5/92	
127	Salton Sea West	Salton City	Imperial	11/21/94	
45	San Diego	San Diego	San Diego	6/9/85	4/27/89
66	San Diego	San Digeo	San Diego	4/27/89	
69	San Jose	San Jose	Santa Clara	6/8/87	
112	San Ardo	San Lucas	Monterey	6/18/93	3/13/95
52	San Luis Obispo	San Luis Obispo	San Luis Obispo	4/2/86	
107	Santa Barbara	Santa Barbara	Santa Barbara	4/7/93	
67	Goleta	Santa Barbara	Santa Barbara	2/17/88	4/7/93
104	De Laveaga	Santa Cruz	Santa Cruz	9/28/90	
38	Santa Maria	Santa Maria	Santa Barbara	5/3/83	
99	Santa Monica	Santa Monica	Los Angeles	12/11/92	
58	Santa Paula	Santa Paula	Ventura	7/30/87	2/15/91
83	Santa Rosa	Santa Rosa	Sonoma	2/11/89	
64	Santa Ynez	Santa Ynez	Santa Barbara	11/21/86	
68	Seeley	Seeley	Imperial	5/29/87	
5	Shafter/USDA	Shafter	Kern	6/1/82	
114	Arroyo Seco	Soledad	Monterey	6/18/93	
28	Soledad	Soledad	Monterey	1/4/83	2/11/87
79	Angwin	St. Helena	Napa	5/11/89	12/27/96
15	Stratford	Stratford	Kings	10/29/82	
57	Buntingville	Susanville	Lassen	6/22/86	
59	Tehachapi	Tehachapi	Kern	7/29/86	8/23/90
130	Temecula East	Temecula	Riverside	7/1/95	11/5/96
137	Temecula East II	Temecula	Riverside	2/20/97	
24	Thermal (inactive)	Thermal	Riverside	11/22/82	3/3/86
50	Thermal	Thermal	Riverside	7/22/86	
105	Westlands	Tranquility	Fresno	4/17/92	
48	Tulelake	Tulelake	Siskiyou	2/3/86	9/30/93
91	Tulelake FS	Tulelake	Siskiyou	4/12/89	
117	Victorville	Victorville	San Bernardino	2/1/94	
33	Visalia/ICI Americas	Visalia	Tulare	1/5/83	
65	Walnut Creek	Walnut Creek	Contra Costa	7/22/87	
111	Green Valley Road	Watsonville	Santa Cruz	5/29/92	
16	San Juan	Watsonville	Monterey	10/23/82	8/24/95
3	Beach / Santa Cruz CO	Watsonville	Santa Cruz	5/30/82	8/25/86
4	Webb / Santa Cruz CO	Watsonville	Santa Cruz	5/30/82	4/29/88
95	Watsonville	Watsonville	Santa Cruz	9/13/89	7/24/95
18	Westmorland	Westmorland	Imperial	11/11/82	4/9/86
103	Windsor	Windsor	Sonoma	12/14/90	
119	Putah Creek	Winters	Solano	8/21/93	1/25/95
27	Zamora	Woodland	Yolo	12/5/82	
96	Woodside	Woodside	San Mateo	10/31/90	1/24/94

The Water Budget

Plants need to replace the amount of water lost through evapotranspiration, or ET. More water than (ET) times the plant factor (Kc) should be considered wasted water. Excess water only contributes to soil, root, nutrient and erosion problems. Excess water becomes expensive as a commodity and causes hidden costs for the customer and the community.

The water budget is one of the contractor's tools for achieving efficient water use, plant health and improved customer service for every site. Too much water is costly to the customer and produces an unhealthy landscape.

When to water a landscape is just as important as how much to water.

Every site differs in soil type, plant materials, root zone depth, irrigation system output and efficiency, environmental factors and microclimates. It is difficult to predict when or how often to water. But, by tracking the water applied to the site, comparing that amount to the ET and using a soil probe to monitor actual field conditions, a contractor can determine site specific parameters for when and how much to water. Remember, irrigation is needed to replace water lost to evapotranspiration. No more water than (ET) times the plant factor, or (Kc), are needed by plants. Any more water is not beneficial to the landscape.

Water Budget Equation

(ET) x (Kc) x (LA) = Site Water Budget

ET – Local evapotranspiration rate

Kc – Site plant factor or crop coefficient

LA – Landscape area

Note: Irrigation inefficiency must be factored into the site water budget equation as shown below:
(I.E. stands for percent Irrigation Efficiency)

$$\frac{(ET) \times (Kc) \times (LA)}{(IE)} = \text{Site Water Budget}$$

*If irrigation efficiency is below 75% then water could be considered wasted. Systems should be upgraded to improve efficiency.

How Much Water is a Site Using – Tracking Site Water Use

Water can not be counted as savings without knowing how much water is actually being used on a site and what the water need, or water budget, is for the landscape. The same information is needed whether it's a separately metered landscape or a mix-metered site. A metered site has monthly water use data available on the water bill. A meter serving both inside and outside water use can be sub-metered to determine actual landscape use. Another method to determine how much water an unmetered site is using in the landscape is to analyze a bill during a rainy month, when outside irrigation is shut off, to determine typical inside water use. The rainy month interior water use number becomes a baseline for site water demand. Monthly landscape irrigation appears as water used over and above the baseline (interior use).

(Top left) A soil probe can be used to monitor actual soil moisture. (Top right) Weekly meter readings show how much water is being applied. It can also identify leaks or system malfunctions. (Above) The irrigation system uniformity must be known to determine the water budget. (Left) Adjust controllers consistently as weather changes.

Water histories are used on weekly site walks.

ctual Site Water Use Compared to Landscape Water Budget:

Landscape Area – 1.17 acres
(no plant material changes during this time period)

Historical ET – 48.2 inches/year

	1990 Use/ET (inches)	1993 Use/ET (inches)	1995 Use/ET (inches)
an	9.8 / 2.1	0.6 / 1.9	1.0 / 1.6
eb	5.7 / 2.4	0.0 / 2.2	0.0 / 1.9
ar	7.9 / 3.4	0.0 / 3.8	0.0 / 3.6
pr	10.4 / 4.9	2.7 / 5.8	2.9 / 5.6
ay	8.7 / 5.3	5.3 / 5.9	5.7 / 4.3
un	12.4 / 5.8	3.2 / 6.2	3.0 / 5.1
ul	7.6 / 6.3	5.9 / 5.5	5.3 / 6.7
ug	13.1 / 6.5	5.7 / 6.2	7.4 / 6.6
ept	8.2 / 4.9	3.7 / 4.3	6.9 / 5.1
ct	9.4 / 3.6	3.3 / 3.4	6.5 / 3.7
ov	8.0 / 2.7	3.3 / 2.7	5.8 / 2.5
ec	8.4 / 1.99	1.3 / 2.4	3.7 / 1.9
otals	Use / ET	Use / ET	Use / ET
	109.6 / 49.9	35.0 / 50.3	48.2 / 48.6
	54% over budget	30% under budget	annual use right on budget

Conversions:

hoose the unit of measurement for specific needs, i.e. use inch-
s as it relates to ET and irrigation application rates, or use
CF as it relates to water billing units for the customer.

nches to CCF - $\frac{(inches)(435.6)}{12} = CCF$ 1 ccf = 748 gallons

CF to Inches - $\frac{(ccf)(12)}{435.6} = inches$ 1 inch (of water) = 36.3 ccf

Comparing Actual Water Used to Landscape Water Budget Needs

The example at left is an actual, separately metered, landscape site. This table compares the actual water used on the site to the actual weather for the same month.

Conclusions/analysis from the site irrigation history:

The water use history of this site is consistent with landscape meters across the state. Too little water is likely used in the spring and early summer months, while too much water is applied in the fall and winter months.

- Based on site size (1.17 acres) and plant materials (60% turf, 40% trees and shrubs) the site requires approximately 100% of ET for one acre of turf for optimum plant health
- Water use, in 1990 (before local water budgets and incentive pricing), was 54.4% higher than the evapotranspiration rate (ET)
- Water use in 1993 was 30% under irrigated with plant health maintained (showing the low water use potential for this landscape during a drought period)

- Water use in 1995 was, in practical terms, identical to the evapotranspiration (ET) requirements of the plant materials on the site
- The landscape is often under irrigated in the early spring, and over irrigated in the fall
- 1990 use wasted at least 1.6 million gallons of water not required by the landscape
- Significant learning by the contractor has taken place to be able to irrigate as per the weather
- Agency water budget and pricing programs motivated the customer and contractor to become efficient water managers
- Customer water bills were reduced significantly without any reduction or change in landscape health and appearance

Tracking a sites water use in comparison to its water needs (ET) is accepted as the method for measuring water efficiency on a site by site basis. With the water use analysis, the contractor has a powerful tool to educate staff and the customer as to the job being done as well as the potential to improve the site. For example, contractors should get paid for the service of tracking water use; get paid for the service of quickly changing irrigation schedules as weather changes; get paid for the service of identifying water leaks quickly and get paid for the service of saving water and lowering water bills for the customer. A water use history/comparison becomes the foundation for development of specific plans for irrigation system upgrades, plant renovation and /or modifications to the maintenance contract specifications. This information helps create "new" business of retrofitting and renovating paid for with water savings.

Seasonal Water Use

How Hot Is It for Plants?

The use of a water budget serves to evaluate landscape irrigation as it relates to actual weather conditions and plant water needs. An alarming trend is seen statewide. Irrigation scheduling does not match actual weather conditions. The result of inaccurate irrigation scheduling costs customers money on water bills and weakens plant health in the landscape.

Landscape water use histories show, generally, underwatering in the spring and early summer months, with overwatering in the fall and winter months (rains impact actual water need.) Irrigation that does not match weather conditions can create shallow rooted turf, stunted trees, increase disease potential and cause high water bills for customers. The following charts show the typical landscape water use pattern:

How often is this site checked? Reading a meter and comparing it to actual ET could help discover this problem before the water bill comes.

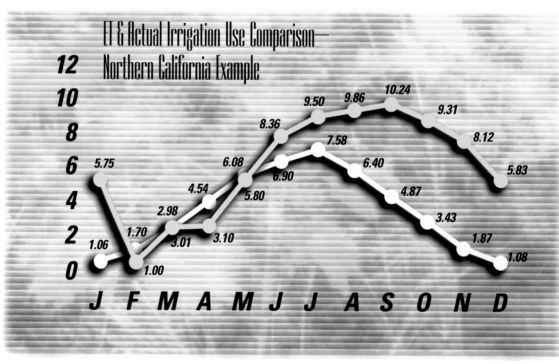

ET & Actual Irrigation Use Comparison—Northern California Example

Values (ET line): 5.75, 1.70, 2.98, 4.54, 6.08, 8.36, 9.50, 9.86, 10.24, 9.31, 8.12, 5.83

Values (Actual line): 1.06, 1.00, 3.01, 3.10, 5.80, 6.90, 7.58, 6.40, 4.87, 3.43, 1.87, 1.08

J F M A M J J A S O N D

ACTUAL Site Water Use (inches)

ET (Evapotranspiration, inches)

Overwatering from June through January shows poor irrigation scheduling habits, even irrigating during rainy months.

Adjust controllers according to actual weather.

Problem:

Landscapes are irrigated by how "hot" it feels to the maintenance staff. Landscapes are underwatered in the spring, when it feels cool, and over irrigated in the fall when temperature and/or winds make it feel hot to people.

Solution:

Monitor the daily, weekly and monthly ET to "know" the actual impact of weather on plants. Use a soil probe to monitor soil moisture. Use a schedule based on actual weather for turning water up or down.

How Hot is it for Plants II –

Spring

Plants need water in spring during the fast root growth stage. Too little water during spring will shorten roots and cause stress during the summer hot months. Use ET to get adequate water deep into the soil. Use irrigation, with rains, to keep the soil moist (not saturated) to build deep root systems.

Fall

The days are shorter, the nights cooler, the sun is lower on the horizon (less solar radiation) and the physiological water needs of plants is decreasing. Weather and plant needs combine to mean that less water is needed by plants even though it may still feel hot to people.

Know the irrigation system, the time it takes for water to run-off, the water needs of the plants and the soil moisture to avoid this scene.

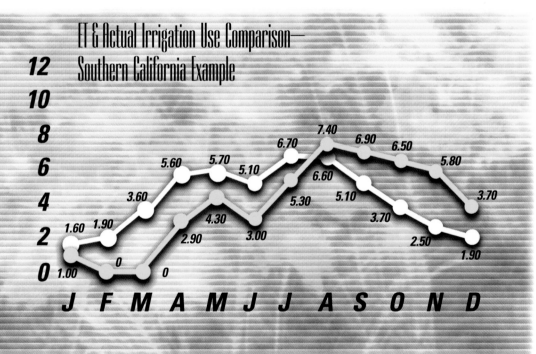

ET & Actual Irrigation Use Comparison— Southern California Example

12
10
8
6
4
2
0

7.40
6.70   6.90   6.50
5.60   5.70   5.10   6.60   5.80
3.60   5.30   5.10   3.70
1.60   1.90   4.30   3.00   3.70   2.50
1.00   0   0   2.90   3.00   1.90

J F M A M J J A S O N D

ACTUAL Site Water Use (inches)

ET (Evapotranspiration, inches)

Over and under reaction to weather changes and rains are typical. Weather changes can be dramatic and need to be tracked for efficiency.

Why do landscapes receive inaccurate seasonal irrigation? A northern California study suggests that there is a disincentive for landscapes to be irrigated to match the weather. Changing irrigation clocks is time consuming and not a priority for contractors. After all, they do not pay the water bill.

Inaccurate seasonal irrigation is simply the inability or inattention to change controllers to match the weather (ET). How often should controllers be changed? As often as significant weather changes dictate. The graph below shows the weekly changes in weather over 3 consecutive years. The percent change is listed in the right-hand column. Weather changes dramatically. Schedules should change to benefit plants.

How Weather (ET) Changes Weekly – 3 Year Comparison

- This year's schedule may not work for next year
- Landscape health improves with accurate watering

What To Do:

- Read water meters
- Use a soil probe
- Track actual ET
- Make appropriate controller changes as weather changes

Week	Year 1 ccf's per week	Year 2 ccf's per week	Year 3 ccf's per week	Percent Change
1	9.08	19.60	9.96	81.68
2	13.07	19.60	4.15	125.88
3	11.62	26.50	1.66	187.33
4	12.34	18.88	9.96	64.98
5	29.77	16.70	6.92	128.39
6	21.42	23.23	17.76	26.29
7	17.79	24.32	11.91	61.27
8	18.15	18.88	17.42	8.04
9	18.88	22.87	11.91	61.27
10	33.03	25.41	7.17	118.24
11	35.57	25.77	10.55	104.41
12	32.67	34.12	29.61	14.04
13	23.23	28.31	13.61	67.69
14	33.76	31.58	52.37	52.99
15	41.75	35.94	50.02	33.07
16	41.02	41.75	54.27	29.01
17	50.82	35.94	50.02	32.64
18	47.19	29.77	56.63	60.32
19	48.28	33.76	50.43	37.75
20	50.46	16.70	56.04	95.08
21	40.66	40.66	56.04	33.59
22	53.72	30.49	34.05	58.93
23	45.52	45.74	43.60	4.76
24	52.64	36.66	58.03	43.51
25	53.72	43.20	48.42	21.71
26	62.07	62.80	60.11	4.36
27	52.27	53.36	61.09	15.87
28	52.27	53.00	60.78	15.37
29	49.01	51.91	66.38	31.15
30	35.94	47.19	69.83	66.47
31	40.66	49.01	68.11	52.19
32	52.64	55.18	66.81	24.34
33	50.82	60.62	67.25	27.58
34	49.73	54.45	63.37	24.42
35	49.01	47.92	65.52	32.50
36	46.10	44.65	60.79	31.95
37	42.83	49.01	47.98	13.26
38	23.60	39.57	41.86	52.16
39	32.67	35.94	36.75	11.62
40	40.29	30.13	34.37	29.09
41	22.87	32.31	35.73	42.44
42	19.97	33.40	25.52	51.07
43	31.22	27.95	23.48	28.09
44	35.21	21.78	26.20	48.43
45	29.40	23.96	13.48	71.45
46	19.24	15.61	18.79	20.30
47	25.05	24.32	14.40	50.10
48	21.78	23.23	15.65	37.49
49	26.14	16.70	19.04	45.77
50	13.07	16.70	9.69	53.29
51	11.98	11.98	10.24	15.26
52	27.59	13.79	14.12	74.59

Total Yearly	1799.59 ccf	1722.85 ccf	1858.98 ccf	
Historical ET	1749 ccf or 48.2 inches of water for cool season turf (30 yr. average)			
Difference from 30 Year avg.	3.25% above average	1.16% above average	6.65% above average	

This "problem" lasted eight weeks. Result: high water bills, customer service problems.

Controllers should be changed if weather changes. And weather will change. Don't guess. Become water managers that "know" how much water to apply to the landscape. Develop site by site water budgets; track site use and compare it to the changing weather and set clocks according to actual weather and plant needs. Use soil probes, weather stations and the Internet to get the information you need. Get paid for that knowledge and service. Market that ability to attract new clients.

Contractors should be paid for efficient water management. If weekly meter readings and controller adjustments are performed, that service should be factored into site contracts. Show the customer that paying for **quality water management will cost less than paying higher water bills** on sites with neglected controllers.

Landscape Irrigation and Drought

Drought inevitably brings water cut-backs, renewed conservation, even water rationing, that directly effects the commercial landscape and home garden. The green industry should not only expect and anticipate drought cycles (as they are normal for California), but treat the growing state population, and its impact on water supplies, as a never ending drought. The California Department of Water Resources (DWR) predicts "chronic" water shortages soon after the year 2000. That prediction assumes normal rainfall and snow pack. That sounds like water shortages, conservation, and maybe even water rationing every single year out into the future.

During past droughts, typical public policy has been to seek cutbacks in landscape water use first. Plants, like people, need a certain amount of water for their physiological requirements. The landscape, like a business or a bank account, has a value. Plants and landscapes help make a healthy and attractive home, and help create the property values in a community. How then, do we maintain the landscape asset during a drought, or any type of water shortage?

First, the contractor must know the water budget of every site. By knowing the site water budget, based on optimum plant performance, the contractor can reduce irrigation to lower, subsistence levels. While landscape aesthetics may suffer, the customer's landscape asset can be retained through a water shortage.

Problem:

Drought increases chronic water shortage projections; 17 of the last 30 years have been critical, dry or below normal precipitation years

Green Industry Goal:

Minimize impact of water shortages or drought years on landscapes and business

Solutions:

Make landscapes water efficient; partner with public agencies on customer incentive programs; support the development of recycled water; learn the water limits of your landscapes; prioritize the most valuable parts of each landscape for using water and be prepared to manage sites with limited water

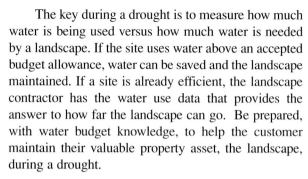

The typical California landscape is adapted to low rain, or drought conditions.

The key during a drought is to measure how much water is being used versus how much water is needed by a landscape. If the site uses water above an accepted budget allowance, water can be saved and the landscape maintained. If a site is already efficient, the landscape contractor has the water use data that provides the answer to how far the landscape can go. Be prepared, with water budget knowledge, to help the customer maintain their valuable property asset, the landscape, during a drought.

Drought may also influence customers to change their landscape style or to use more sophisticated irrigation technologies. Both options mean the need for green industry and contractor assistance and offers a "new" business opportunity. Change is always an opportunity for those businesses that are ready and responsive to the marketplace. Remember, neither you nor the landscape cause drought and you shouldn't feel guilty about a business that utilizes water. Instead, be prepared to help serve customer needs and solve customer problems related to water shortages and conservation mandates.

Using Recycled Water in the Landscape

Reclaimed or recycled water is a major, potential source of water that can be used directly on landscapes. In the city of Irvine, California, 80% of commercial, city, school, golf course and home-owner association landscape acres use recycled water. The community landscapes are viewed as drought resistant, not because of the types of plants in use, but because the source of the recycled water is constant, come rain or drought. Sewage water is treated to a tertiary level (as described in the California Water Code, Title 22) and is determined to be safe for use by the California Department

of Health. Local county health departments permit the use of tertiary treated recycled water for a variety of uses. Recycled water, for example, can be used for swimming, which assumes gulping of the water and for use on agricultural crops. The use of recycled water for landscaping expands the water supply in a way that directly benefits the green industry.

Green industry businesses should become aware of any local recycled water projects or plans, and support efforts to expand the use of recycled water in California (For more information, contact the WateReuse Association.). If recycled water is available in your area, the supplying agency will provide water quality reports that list the constituents and quality of the water. The elements you need to be aware of for plant health are boron, chloride, sodium, nitrates, the sodium absorption ratio (SAR), the electrical conductivity (EC) and the overall total dissolved salts (TDS).

(Above) Recycled water use in a nursery.

(Right) Purple pipe designated for recycled water use.

Remember, with population growth alone, California is heading toward consistent water shortages in the next century. Where will landscapes get the water they need? Recycled water is perhaps the best and most cost-effective new source of water for landscapes.

Misconceptions about Recycled Water:

- It smells
- It will damage plants
- It clogs irrigation systems
- It leads to salt build-up in the soil
- It's unsafe for human contact

Reality of Recycled Water:

- Recycled water has been used right up to the front door of homes in associations, in schools and parks for at least the past 30 years. Recycled water is also used in nurseries to grow ornamental container stock. Recycled water is safe for people and plants when used in landscapes.

- Recycled water, based on actual use in landscapes and from tests at Marin Water District and U.C. Davis, does not damage or hinder landscape plant growth. Studies show that recycled water may actually increase landscape plant growth due to the higher concentrations of nitrogen occurring in the water.

- In areas where recycled water has been used on landscapes for 30 years, no soil salt build-up has been found, even in areas with typically heavy clay soils

- Tertiary treated recycled water is being used with all types of irrigation equipment, including drip and sub-surface irrigation, with no more problems than the same equipment has when the source is potable drinking water.

- Recycled water is used on agricultural crops across the state. Studies show that recycled water is totally safe for crops grown for human consumption.

- Nurseries that use recycled water have never reported any adverse health impact with workers in close contact with recycled water.

The bottom line is that recycled water is safe to use for landscapes and significantly increases the supply of water available for landscapes.

How is Recycled Water Being Used in California?

Miscellaneous 8%

Industry 2%

Landscape 12%

Agriculture 21%

Environmental 8%

Seawater Intrusion Barrier 2%

Groundwater Recharge 47%

Hidden Cost of Over-Watering

It is true that too much water can damage the landscape and kill more plants than under-watering ever does. Over-watering may stunt plant growth, may help bring on chlorosis, leaches nutrients from the soil, makes nutrients unavailable to plants, contributes to shallow rooting and soil compaction. Those are obvious horticultural problems caused by over-watering. There are other, more costly problems:

● High costs to customers for water not needed by plants

● Degradation of asphalt in streets and parking lots

● Pollutants washed into other water bodies (streams, estuaries, bays and ocean) from water run-off

● Damage to fences, hardscapes and building structures

The combination of hidden costs make over-watering costly to customers and communities. For example, one city analyzed all maintenance costs in the public works department. It found that significant dollars were being spent every year to repair street potholes and asphalt. The major cause of the street problems were coming from the over spray and water run-off from the adjacent streetscapes. Even relatively new landscapes and irrigation systems contributed to the problem. The answer for the city was to find a more cost effective way to irrigate valuable community landscaping and save streets at the same time. The city solutions included:

● New street landscape design guidelines with emphasis on efficient irrigation technology and plants that require less water

● Making routine street upgrades that include landscape and irrigation renovations to eliminate overspray and run-off

● Landscape maintenance specifications that have been rewritten to incorporate ET water budgeting as the accepted irrigation scheduling method, and to make landscape irrigators responsible for high water use penalties

Population increases will mean water shortages even in non-drought years.

(Right) Efficient landscapes can be attractive and colorful.

(Below) Low-water-use and low-maintenance home landscapes fit customer desires.

The public is looking for unique and efficient plants.

The Bottom Line

The cost to customers and communities from over-watering can be staggering. The green industry is responsible for the design, installation and maintenance of landscapes, whether they are efficient or wasteful. Therefore, the green industry must take the lead in providing solutions to help eliminate the hidden and high costs caused by the excessive use of water in the landscape.

The bottom line is what determines the actions and priorities any business makes. Each and every green industry business can decide how to be competitive in a state where water is precious. It is the hope of the groups that commissioned and produced this guide that the information presented here will assist you to: (1) be better informed, (2) have greater confidence to provide a water efficient landscape for your customers, (3) market your services and abilities to increase business in a state with a future of water limits.

This guide book is based on positive examples of what the green industry has to offer and can do for customers faced with water budgets in California. Hopefully, this effort will inspire readers to seek out the information they need from local experts, schools and public agencies. To address state water demand and supply circumstances, public needs will change. Business will need to adapt and change to keep pace. Businesses' profit when market forces drive change and the business is ready to serve the new need.

Be ready. Prepare now and establish your business as a leader that performs for the customer. The future is clear. Water will be key to California prosperity, environment and quality of life. The green industry can provide quality service to every water customer by striving for water efficiency on each and every site. Use this guide, university information, local colleges, public agencies and the services of specialized green industry consultants to reach water efficiency in every landscape.

Integrated Management Program Calendar Example

Seasons	FALL									WINTER										
Month	SEP	OCT				NOV				DEC				JAN				FEB		
Start Date	23	1	8	16	23	1	8	16	23	1	8	16	23	1	8	16	23	1	8	16
System Maintenance																				
Pressure																				
Adjust Pressure Regulator[1]	■																		■	
Adjust Control Valves[2]	■																		■	
Field Adjustments																				
Sprinkler Height[3]			■																	■
Sprinkler Arcs and Nozzles[4]			■																	
Irrigation Scheduling[5]		■				■				■				■				■		
Cultural Practices																				
Evaluate Soil Moisture[6]				■																
Deep Irrigation[7]				■																
Aerification[8]				■																
Fertilization																				
Winter Blend[9]										■					■					
Granular–High Iron[10]				■																
Soil Amendment[11]																				
Weed Control[12]	■																			■
Spot Treatment[13]																				

Legend:

- *Recommended* ■
- *When Needed* ■
- *Bermuda, Kikuya When Needed* ■
- *Pre-Emergent When Needed* ■

1. Adjust pressure regulator so that the system operating pressure is equal irrigati design pressure shown on irrigation plans or not more than 20% above press required to maintain sprinkler head operating pressure at the worst hydraulic c dition.

2. Adjust control valve throttling device so that farthest and highest sprinkler he operates at the manufacturer's optimum operating pressure or as indicated on irrigation plans.

3. Adjust sprinkler heads in turf areas so that the top of the sprinkler head is flush 1/4" above finish grade. For shrub and ground cover areas adjust riser height avoid interference from adjacent plant foliage.

4. Make sure sprinkler arcs and nozzles are appropriate for the intended landsca type. Size nozzle for intended spacing.

5. Adjust irrigation schedules monthly. Reprogram controllers as needed to m actual evapo-transpiration requirements.

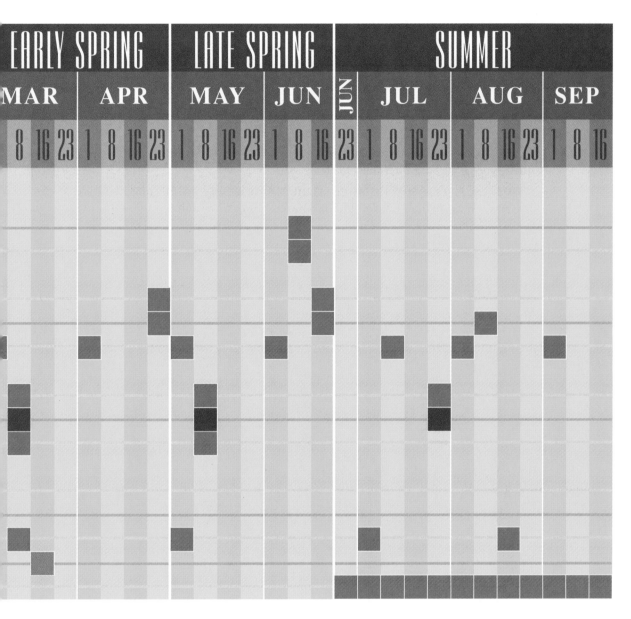

EARLY SPRING							LATE SPRING								SUMMER													
MAR			APR				MAY				JUN			JUN	JUL				AUG				SEP		

Determine depth of soil moisture and overall soil moisture content with a soil probe.

Irrigate turf to 6" depth before aerification and after fertilization.

Aerify at least 2-1/2" deep no more than 48 hours before fertilization.

Apply winter blend fertilizer with nitrate nitrogen w/potassium (22-3-9).

Apply granular material with approximately equal amounts of N and Fe (9-9-9).

Apply soil amendments combining 1/4" screen high-quality humus at 200lbs/1,000 sq.ft. and inorganic material for increased water holding capacity.

12. Prevent weed with pre-emergent. Remove unwanted grass weeds such as bermuda, kikuya with chemical spray. Replant with seed or sod. Control established broadleaf weeds with overall spray.

13. Treat dry areas that do not respond to irrigation system maintenance through aerification and soil amendments.

Source: Pagano and Barry (1996)

Example Landscape Maintenance Specifications for a Water and Resource Efficient Landscape

The following landscape maintenance specifications were designed for a real world homeowner association and have been implemented on the site.

Use these typical specifications as an example only. When combined with site specific numbers, the specifications offer the opportunity to establish high quality customer service and receive payment for those important services. It may be appropriate to enlist the assistance of a specialized water manager to evaluate irrigation systems, develop preventative irrigation system maintenance programs and set irrigation schedules.

This is a specifications example only. It should be understood that the weather, soils, plant materials and other specific site features may require careful analysis of maintenance schedules, fertilization and irrigation for optimum plant health.

These specifications are intended to show how to take information from this book and case studies and apply them to specifications for bidding and contract development. The intent of these model specifications are to: (1) develop specifications that help meet the need to maintain landscapes within a water budget; (2) upgrade industry standards and receive payment for more sophisticated work; (3) provide a road map for contractors and customers to set goals, measure the site efforts and keep costs in line for both parties.

Section One—Water Efficient Specification

Table of Contents

III. Scope of Work

Section Two—Water Efficient Specification

I. Introduction

1.01 Project Concepts

Contractor, responsible for the maintenance of the landscape areas, seeks to provide an attractive, colorful and resource efficient landscape for the benefit of the Customer.

The Customer expects a high standard of horticultural service to maintain the landscape. These standards are detailed in the Landscape Maintenance Specifications. The specifications include the use of an integrated management program of soil, water, irrigation system, fertilization and pest management that optimizes plant health, resource efficiency and, therefore, cost-effectiveness for the site and the Customer.

1.02 Site Map

A site map will be provided and shared between the Customer and Contractor. The map shall reflect general plant palette, plant associations (i.e. hydrozones), streets and addresses. Copies of the map shall be on file with the Customer and Contractor, and will be used to identify locations of work to be performed, locate problems, etc.

1.03 Irrigation Map

A map describing the existing irrigation system including location of meters, valves, controllers, quick couplers and the types (brands) of irrigation equipment utilized on the site.

1.04 Site Plant List

A list of all existing plants will be included and on file with the Customer and Contractor. The list is to be used as a reference for plant replacements, to identify plants that do not meet the standards of the association and to help determine potential plants to add to the site when appropriate.

1.05 Emergency Phone Numbers

All phone numbers, including those of the Customer and Contractor, shall be listed, including numbers for 24 hour emergency service.

Section Three—Water Efficient Specification

II. General Requirements

2.01 Protection of Existing Structures and Property

Contractor shall take proper precautions when working on-site to protect any and all association structures, infrastructure and utilities. Any damages to association structures will be reported immediately to the customer's Representative. Any damages caused by Contractor action shall be corrected and/or paid for by the Contractor at no cost to the Customer.

2.02 Safety

Contractor shall adhere to all state, federal and local requirements related to the safe completion of all work. Contractor safety includes the use of safety gear, traffic control and vehicle safety.

2.03 Customer

The Customer shall have authority to call meetings, with a 24 hour advance notice, for purposes of discussing site issues, performance and needs. Contractor shall provide reports, as designated in the scope of work, to the Customer.

2.04 Maintenance Schedule/Inspection Schedule

Contractor shall provide service to the association with time to be negotiated. The hours spent on site to be determined by the scope of work desired by the Customer. The Customer and Contractor shall participate in monthly site review/inspections.

2.05 Contractor Supervision

Contractor shall provide qualified on-site supervision to insure high quality work and provide accurate reports.

2.06 Extra Work

Work determined to be beyond the tasks listed in the scope of work shall be "extra" work.

Extra work will be planned, estimated and proposed to the Customer for authorization before performing the work ("extra" work should be designated and clearly understood at the initiation of the contract.)

2.07 Plant Material Replacement

Plant materials may require replacement for safety, aesthetics or because of damages. All replacement plant materials shall be in keeping with the association plant list, or approved substitutions. Color plants will need periodic or seasonal replacement and renewal.

2.08 Pesticide Regulations

All chemicals shall be used in strict accordance with federal, state, county and local laws and regulations. Any use of chemicals shall be reported to the Customer and applied by trained and licensed pest control operators. It is the intent of the association to maintain a healthy, sustainable landscape that will minimize the need for and use of chemical controls. An Integrated Pest Management Program (IPM) and biological controls will be utilized as much as possible for the site (*design an IPM approach for your specific situation).

2.09 Fertilizer Regulations

Contractor shall adhere to the fertilizer programs described in the scope of work. The intent is to use the minimum amount of fertilizers necessary to produce a healthy and attractive landscape. Contractor shall take soil samples in a variety of hydrozones and locations to determine the actual need for soil/plant nutrients before applying fertilizer. The frequency of fertilization is set by the results of the soil sampling.

2.10 Weed Control

Contractor is responsible for keeping all areas free of weeds. Contractor is required to keep weeds controlled by (1) the use of organic mulches on the soil surface, (2) manual labor, and (3) chemical controls, in that order.

2.11 Soil Analysis

Contractor shall perform a soil fertility test at least twice per year or before major fertilization, as designated in the scope of work. The primary goal is to apply fertilizer only if the soil is found to be without adequate nutrients for plant vigor. The intent is to reduce overall fertilizer application to keep salt build-up potential low, to minimize excessive plant growth that requires more maintenance time, water and fertilization.

2.12 Method of Payment

(insert appropriate data)

2.13 Water Penalty Charges

(For future use in areas where water budgets are established by the water purveyor.)

Water penalty charges are to be the responsibility of the Contractor. Only those water penalties accrued due to over-water-use behavior (i.e. water management, not leaks, vandalism or malfunctioning irrigation equipment) will count toward Contractor responsibility. With a 100% ET water budget allocation, it is assumed that the site landscape can maintain health and meet water use goals. An inefficient irrigation system must be recognized as a major barrier to meeting water budget allocations. (Bonuses could be awarded to the Contractor, at the discretion of the Customer, for meeting water budgets or using less water than the site water budget allocation suggests.)

2.14 Licensing

Contractor shall maintain a valid C-27 license from the State of California. Contractor shall also hold appropriate Pest Control Operators and chemical application licensing/certification or provide services of same as part of this contract.

2.15 Insurance

Contractor shall provide proof of insurance and adhere to the following limits of liability: (Use appropriate numbers as per customer requirements, such as: Worker's Compensation, statutory limits; Automobile Collision, $1 million; Comprehensive General Liability, $1 million).

2.16 Notice of Cancellation

The landscape maintenance contract is subject to 30 day written notice of cancellation by either party.

Section Four—Water Efficient Specification

III. Scope of Work

The scope of work contained herein establishes a standard of landscape care for the Customer. The scope is specifically intended to produce an attractive, healthy and cost effective landscape. Contractor shall furnish all labor, equipment, materials, tools and specific skills required to perform the scope of work set forth in the maintenance specifications.

3.01 Soil Management Program

Soils Analysis: Contractor shall provide a soil fertility test at least twice per year, or before major fertilization, (example: March, October) for help to determine proper fertilization needs.

Soil Probe Analysis: The site supervisor and site personnel shall utilize a hand soil probe to physically determine soil moisture levels in various planting zones. The soil probe analysis is to be used (along with water meter readings and irrigation scheduling software) to monitor and adjust site irrigation schedules, to find wet or dry stations as well as to observe plant root depth and development.

3.02 Water Management Program

The water management program is intended to maximize plant health, minimize water damages to association hardscape and property, and eliminate any over-water use.

1. Contractor shall consistently maintain all components of the irrigation system in proper working order, as per manufacturers specifications, by inspecting the entire system on an ongoing basis.

2. Drip lines and spray heads shall be randomly checked on an ongoing basis such that the entire system is checked each month. Malfunctioning systems will be corrected immediately. Methods of detection include: visual sightings of water on association hardscape and property, soil probing, meter monitoring and specific line observations.

3. Irrigation controllers and irrigation scheduling shall be performed regularly as weather changes (ET), plant needs and water budget allocations (100% ET) to avoid water penalty charges. Rescheduling may be required as frequently as on a weekly basis depending on weather conditions.

4. Irrigation system pressure shall be checked and adjusted at least monthly to insure efficient operation of irrigation stations.

5. All irrigation replacement parts shall be as original installation or approved equals.

6. Turf spray heads shall be uniform in output and kept adjusted for accurate throw. If the irrigation is not adequate to provide uniform coverage and ability to meet water budgets, the Customer agrees to upgrade the system to achieve site efficiency.

7. Contractor shall list and report all irrigation system damages to the Customer with the cost estimate of repair/replacement.

8. Contractor shall track and provide to the customer an irrigation scheduling log that tracks the amount of water applied to various site hydrozones. The Contractor may choose to use irrigation scheduling and monitoring software of their choice to determine water schedules.

9. The water budget allocation for the association grounds is 100% of actual weather (ET or evapotranspiration) multiplied by the site acreage. Based on the water needs of the majority of plant materials and the use of efficient irrigation systems, it is assumed that water use can and will consistently fall below the 100% ET allocation. Appropriate water management will produce a healthier landscape and save significant costs.

10. For weather based irrigation scheduling, Contractor shall use software that will track and report water applications on a station by station basis and that can compare actual water use to local ET.

11. Irrigation scheduling will be performed to encourage deep roots, including deep watering through use of multiple repeat cycles. Soil probing shall be used to determine soil moisture depth, overall moisture levels and the need to adjust irrigation schedules. Soils will be allowed to dry to a 50% moisture depletion level between irrigations in order to avoid root-rot and allow adequate air to be present in the soil.

12. Irrigation scheduling will be coordinated with all other maintenance activities, including mowing, aeration and fertilization.

3.03 Turf Management Program

The goal of the turf management program is to maximize plant health, deepen turf roots, water as per local ET and reduce the frequency of fertilization, mowing, dump fees and water run-off.

1. Mowing cycles may vary from 5 days (early Spring through Summer) to 10 days (late Fall through Winter) between cuttings. Varied mowing cycles are derived from Best Management Practice's for healthy turf and seasonal growth habits of cool season grasses.

2. Contractor shall use grasscycling (the use of mulching mowers to keep grass clippings on-site) as the preferred method of turf clipping disposal. (Grasscycling adds nutrients to soil and reduces labor time, transportation and dump fees.) Grasscycling need not be used when turf growth is considered too high (as after rain and mowing delays). To insure attractive and effective use of grasscycling , mow no more than 1/3 of turf height at any mowing.

3. Turf areas shall be edged as needed to maintain appearance. Turf spray nozzles shall be of a height to clear the highest unmowed turf growth height. (see 3.02, 6.)

4. Aerification shall be performed in turf areas to promote deep rooting, water penetration and to avoid soil compaction. Aerification shall be performed as per the following schedule: early Spring (March/April), early Summer (June) and early Fall (mid September to early October). Turf aerification shall be accompanied by complimentary cultural practices (i.e. top dressing with organic material and deep watering schedules) to insure the highest quality turf appearance and water efficiency. Cultural practices in combination with aerification and schedules are as follows:

   Day 1 – irrigate turf normally

Day 2 – mow grass normally

Day 3 – aerify at least to 3 inch depth {deeper if possible with equipment and soil type}

Day 4 – add organic top dressing and fertilizer to turf, water normally

5. Turf fertilizers shall be applied within the range of 3-4 lb. per 1000 sq.ft. of actual Nitrogen per year, 3 lb. of Potassium per 1000 sq.ft. per year, 3 lb. of Iron per 1000 sq.ft. per year for cool season grass if and when soils tests suggest. (The goal is to reduce Nitrogen applied to turf in order to moderate growth and keep water needs down. This can be accomplished through the use of organic based and slow release fertilizers that contain Iron to maintain deep green color. See 3.03, 7.)

6. Aerification amendment is designed to (1) improve soil quality in turf areas, (2) allow deeper water penetration, (3) allow deeper turf root growth, (4) reduce water applications for turf, and (5) gradually reduce fertilizer applications for turf. The amendment shall be added to all turf areas using the above schedule. The amendment type and amount shall approximate the following directions: screened compost, such as Aguinaga Turf Plus, at 150 - 200 lb. per 1000 sq.ft. {use of amendment can be reduced over time as top dressing adds nutrients to the soil}.

3.04 Shrub Management Program

The goal of the shrub program is to develop a lush, natural appearance, promote flowering and keep pruning and trimming to a minimum for cost-effectiveness for the Customer.

1. Pruning shall be done on an as needed basis only. The intent of this style of pruning is to maintain the natural plant appearance. Shrubs are intended to fill planting spaces as much as possible. Shrubs on slopes are not to be pruned or shaped, but are to be allowed to spread naturally.

2. Shearing back of shrub stems and branches is not encouraged unless the plant poses a safety hazard, or unless directed by the Customer.

3. Shrub irrigation will approximate WUCOLS (Appendix V) water use recommendations for typical shrub species, generally 50% of local ET.

4. Shrub fertilization shall be performed using slow release, complete organic based products in April and October, or as indicated by the soil test results. Spot fertilization may be applied to color plants to encourage flowering.

5. All vines shall be kept "pinned" to fences or walls to maximize hardscape cover and provide green appearance.

6. Shrub list with specific actions included: ***Example Only!!!***
    Agapanthus – remove dead flower stalks shortly after flowers fade
    Calliandra – keep pinned to walls and fences, let spread to cover as much area as possible
    Daylily – cut dead flower stalks after bloom cycle ends, clean out old leaves monthly
    Liriope – no trimming needed, old leaves will periodically need removal
    Moraea – cut spent flower stalks after blooming, keep tip burn controlled as much as possible by (1) using Chelated Iron, and leaf trimming as needed
    Nandina – no pruning needed
    Rahpiolepis – no pruning required unless plant spreads out of planting space and causes a nuisance
    Sword Fern – no pruning necessary, may require thinning, intended to fill dark planting spaces
    Trumpet vine – keep pinned to walls and fences, let spread to cover as much area as possible

3.05 Groundcover Management Program

The site groundcovers are intended to fill large common space areas, provide significant color, present a lush appearance.

1. All groundcover areas shall be uniformly irrigated to insure consistent growth and plant coverage.

2. Groundcover areas shall be kept free of weeds and grasses.

3. Irrigation will approximate WUCOLS recommendation levels for the species.

4. Sparse groundcover areas will be checked for, (1) soil moisture levels, (2) irrigation coverage, to

Example Fertilization Program:

- **Fall** – 9-9-9 with 11% Iron
- **Winter** – Ammonium Nitrate (water soluble) with 22-3-9
- **Spring** – Balanced fertilization, 9-9-9
- **Summer** – Balanced, organic, slow release w/ Iron

help determine growth problem. Bare areas may require hand tilling of soil, addition of amendment and replanting to create plant uniformity.

5. Fertilization shall be done with a complete, organic based, slow release product.

6. Groundcover list includes: ***Example Only!!!***

Honeysuckle – requires annual cutback to avoid woody appearance, use complete fertilizer with Iron; chlorosis may mean too much water

Star Jasmine – will require trimming in small planter areas to be neat, preferred approach is to use consistent hand clipping of long stems (as opposed to mechanical shearing), plants against walls can be allowed to spread for maximum cover at the discretion of the customer.

Geranium – will require annual (winter) cutback to encourage new growth and flowering, should be used as a filler and accent among other groundcovers and shrubs, may require "blooming" fertilizer to maximize color, is a relatively short lived plant but is used in conjunction with other groundcovers and shrubs.

3.06 Tree Management Program

The association seeks to maximize the growth and health of tree species, while minimizing damages typically caused by trees or by the lack of proper tree care.

1. All new trees shall be staked to allow movement (at least 6") in the wind. Stakes shall be removed as soon as trees are deemed established in the soil or by one year of planting, whichever comes first.

2. Trees shall be deep watered to encourage deep roots and discourage surface root damages. Deep watering is especially important during the warm months (May-September). Soil moisture and moisture depth shall be checked by hand soil probes. Irrigation will approximate WUCOLS recommendations for trees at levels approximately 50% of local ET.

3. Trees shall be fertilized in accordance with shrub fertilizer program.

4. Trees shall be pruned back only for safety or structural clearance, otherwise, pruning shall be performed as a "thinning" or "opening" to promote tree spread and shading potential. No more than 1/4 to 1/3 of leaf area shall be removed at any pruning. (International Society of Arboriculture standards to guide all tree pruning.)

5. Potential damages caused by tree roots will be identified on site walks. Where appropriate, root pruning shall be performed to avoid costly damages for the Customer.

6. Trees causing consistent physical damage or nuisance can be recommended for removal. Contractor shall report/recommend such hazards to the Customer.

7. Tree List: ***Example Only!!!***

Carrotwood – Evergreen, thin in Winter months on a three year cycle, this tree can take stem and branch cut back to control spread in small areas, may need root pruning in some locations to stop hardscape damages.

Coral – Evergreen, needs preventive maintenance pruning of crossing and weak crotch limbs, thin in Spring annually as needed, avoid drastic stump cutback, root prune to eliminate hardscape damages.

Crepe Myrtle – Deciduous, thin or prune to shape only in Winter, summer flower

Eucalyptus – Evergreen, do not top or cut back severely, thin only. If too large for space, remove entire tree.

Gleditsia – Deciduous, naturally open tree, allow to spread over streets, very little care, tip pruning can help raise branch heights (removes weight)

Koelrueteria – Deciduous, wants to be a large canopy tree, has deep root characteristic, can be pruned (Winter) to scale back size and /or thinned to open, flowers in late Summer with colorful bracts in Fall, will provide attractive shade if allowed to grow to size.

Pine – Evergreen, consistently check for spider mites, control with water spray, bio-control, and/or chemical spray, little to no pruning, may want to thin to remove dead needles yearly, may need root pruning to avoid hardscape damages.

Pistache – Deciduous, Fall color, allow to branch out and spread, slow grower, deep root characteristics, may need selected pruning to shape, let grow for some years before thinning.
Tabebuia – Deciduous, small tree, bright yellow flowers in Spring, naturally open,
prune only to shape.
Tristania – Evergreen, thin or prune in Winter, can take branch cut back to encourage new growth where needed.

3.07 Green Waste/Trash Program

1. All green waste shall be taken to a green waste composting facility (exchanged for composted material if possible).

2. All shrub, tree and groundcover areas are to be kept clear of trash and debris.

3. Use of blowers is prohibited unless otherwise specified by the Customer. The removal of leaves from under shrubs is not necessary due to use of mulch. Street and parking pad leaves may be swept into mulch areas or picked up. Leaves falling into mulch areas (natural leaf drop) shall be left in the mulch unless otherwise directed by Owners Representative.

3.08 Mulching Program

1. Soils in all shrub, tree and groundcover areas, shall be kept covered with organic, shredded, composted mulch. Landscape areas will naturally experience loss or "breakdown" of mulch. This is caused by the natural micro-biotic action of decomposition. This action is exactly what improves and adds to soil quality, however, replacement of mulch to all areas will be required on an as needed basis. A minimum of a 2" layer of mulch is to be kept "up" at all times. This mulch program will also help eliminate weed growth. As shrubs grow to fill in planter spaces, less mulch will be needed. (Leaf drop under shrub plantings adds to the "natural" mulching of the site.)

2. Soil may need to be removed (and plants replaced) where soil is significantly higher than adjacent hardscapes and mulch is consistently kicked and/or washed out. This will produce catchment to help keep mulch in place.

3.09 Integrated Management Program

To insure maximum management impact for the Customer, an integrated management program shall be implemented. Integration relates to all aspects of the maintenance program. Each specific practice impacts all other practices. Examples of complimentary or integrated actions include:

1 Turf watering and mowing schedule – shut off turf watering stations 24 -48 hours before scheduled mowing; water within 24 hours after mowing.

2. Observe and analyze turf growth to determine appropriate mowing schedule (5-10 day window of mowing as season dictates), for maximum plant health, root growth and appearance.

3. Follow the water/mow/aerify/amend schedule in 3.03 for seasonal turf care.

4. Use grasscycling and soil test analysis to help reduce fertilizer frequency.

5. Use aerification, amendment and organic based, slow release fertilizers with Iron to moderate turf growth.

6. Schedule irrigation as per weather (ET) to produce the most attractive and cost effective turf for the Customer.

7 Use seasonal soil analysis to determine the actual need and application rates for fertilization before fertilizing.

8. Perform preventive maintenance checks on a regular basis to avoid major pest, disease, water related or root damage problems. Specifically check for observable evidence of pests or diseases, observe plant leaf color for nutrient deficiency signs, probing the soil to monitor moisture, read water meters weekly to check for unusually high water consumption (a sign of a leak or poor scheduling) and compare readings to actual ET data.

Reference Guide

The following organizations, public institutions and landscape professionals contributed to the development of this handbook.

The California Landscape Contractors Association (CLCA)

CLCA Resource Management Committee:

John Addink	Jerry Allison	Dennis Pittenger
John Basanese	Scott Harris	Larry Rolhfes (CLCA)
Pat Marion	Doug Nakamura	Jeffrey Sheehan
David Norred	Linda Novy	Edward Wallace

The California Department of Water Resources

The Municipal Water District of Orange County (MWDOC)

The Irvine Ranch Water District (IRWD)

Contra Costa Water Agency, Chris Dundon, Landscape Program Coordinator

Las Virgenes Municipal Water District, Scott Harris, Landscape Program Specialist

James Barry, Barry Consulting
(Horticultural instructor, arborist and landscape researcher; provided data on turf and ET study root depth and maintenance programs.)

Integrated Urban Forestry
(Specializing in water and resource efficiency in landscapes, urban forestry and green waste recycling; provided information on soils, cost and benefits of appropriate maintenance.)

Toni Monzon – Bilingual Training Institute
(Provides specialized irrigation training in English and Spanish; tested book chapter on students and industry professionals.)

Dave Pagano – d.d. Pagano & Associates, Irrigation Design
(Specializing in irrigation design, irrigation scheduling, centralized controller operation, retrofits and water management; provided data on irrigation scheduling and field studies.)

Soil and Plant Laboratory
(Provided soil testing data and evaluations for this publication.)

Water Right Soil Probes
(Donated 18' soil probes for the home use study and offers affordable probes for homeowners and professionals.)

This publication is available through The Municipal Water District of Orange County (MWDOC):

> *MWDOC*
> *10500 Ellis Avenue*
> *Fountain Valley, CA 92728*
> *(714) 963-3058*

For information regarding products and consultants listed please call: Tom Ash (714) 669-4303, e-mail toma@ctsicorp.com

APPENDICES III

Bibliography

California Water Plan Update, Volume 1; Bulletin 160-93. Department of Water Resources, State of California. October 1994.

Urban Water Use in California; Bulletin 166-4. Department of Water Resources, State of California. August 1994

The Landscape Below Ground; Proceedings on Tree Root Development in Urban Soils. The International Society of Arboriculture, 1994.

California Landscape Standards. California Landscape Standards Committee, California Landscape Contractors Association.

Landscape Water Audit Evaluation; Contra Costa Water District. Submitted by WATERTECH, August 1994.

CIMIS Urban Resource Book. Department of Water Resources, State of California. January 1996.

Efficient Turfgrass Management: Findings From The Irvine Spectrum Water Conservation Study. Study conducted by d.d. Pagano, James Barry; Statistical Analysis Prepared by Western Policy Research. Submitted to Metropolitan Water District, May 1997.

Saving Water in Landscape Irrigation, Leaflet 2976. Division of Agricultural Science, University of California, 1977.

California Turfgrass Culture; Managing Turfgrasses During Drought, Volume 40; University of California Cooperative Extension. M. Ali Harivandi, Victor A.Gibeault. 1990.

Managing Compacted and Layered Soils; Leaflet 2635. Division of Agricultural Sciences, University of California. April 1979.

California Turfgrass: It's Use, Water Requirement and Irrigation. University of California Cooperative Extension; Victor A. Gibeault, Stephen Cockerham, J. Michael Henry, Jewell Meyer. June 1990.

Gardening for Dummies; Michael McCaskey and the National Gardening Association; IDG Books, 1996.

Water Conservation in Landscaping Ordinance, AB325, 1991.

The California Water Plan Update, Department of Water Resources 160-98 (Draft).

APPENDICES IV
Index

APPENDICES V

WUCOLS (Water Use Classification of Landscape Species) – A Guide to the Water Needs of Landscape Plants

Revised 4/1/94 – An update version will be available by 1999, contact any UCCE office
L.R. Costello – University of California Cooperative Extension
K.S. Jones – University of California Cooperative Extension

PERSPECTIVE: This project was initiated and funded by the Water Conservation Office of the California Department of Water Resources. The work was performed by the University of California Cooperative Extension (San Francisco and San Mateo County Office) in cooperation with 32 landscape professionals.

PURPOSE: To provide guidance to landscape professionals in selecting and maintaining plants based on their irrigation water needs.

INTENDED USE: The WUCOLS list is intended solely as a guide to help landscape professionals identify irrigation water needs of landscape species. It can be used either for the selection of species or to assist in developing irrigation schedules for existing landscapes.

In addition, the evaluations of irrigation water requirements presented here should not be considered absolute and are not intended to be used as such, i.e., the user is not "required" to use these evaluations. This is a guide to species water needs.

ACKNOWLEDGEMENTS: We thank Marsha Prillwitz of the Department of Water Resources, U.S. Bureau of Reclamation for her support, assistance, and encouragement.

Vegetation Types

T	Tree
S	Shrub
V	Vine
G	Groundcover
P	Perennial *(Includes ferns, grasses & bulbs)*

WUCOLs Regions

1	North Central Coastal
2	Central Valley
3	South Coastal
4	South Inland Valley
5	High & Intermediate Desert
6	Low Desert

Invasive Species

★	Greater Statewide Concern
☆	Lesser Statewide Concern

Categories of Water Needs

H	High
M	Moderate
L	Low
VL	Very Low
/	Inappropriate
?	Unknown

	TYPE	BOTANICAL NAME	COMMON NAME	REGIONAL EVALUATIONS					
				1	2	3	4	5	6
	S	Abelia 'Edward Goucher'	pink abelia	M	M	M	M	/	M
	S	Abelia floribunda	Mexican abelia	M	M	M	M	/	/
	S	Abelia X grandiflora	glossy abelia	L	L	M	M	/	M
	Gc	Abelia grandiflora prostrata	prostrate glossy abelia	M	M	M	M	/	/
	S	Abelia 'Sherwoodii'	Sherwood dwarf abelia	M	M	M	M	/	/
	T	Abies spp.	fir	M	/	M	M	/	/
	T	Abies pinsapo	Spanish fir	L	/	L	/	/	/
	S	Abutilon hybridum	flowering maple	M	H	H	H	/	/
	S T	Acacia abyssinica	Abyssinian acacia	/	?	/	?	/	L
	T	Acacia aneura	mulga	/	?	?	?	/	L
☆	T	Acacia baileyana	Bailey acacia	L	L	L	L	/	/
	T S	Acacia berlandieri	guajillo	?	?	?	M	/	L
	T	Acacia cognata (A.subporosa)	bower wattle	L	L	M	M	/	/
	T S	Acacia constricta	whitethorn acacia	?	L	L	L	L	L
	T S	Acacia craspedocarpa	leatherleaf acacia	?	?	?	?	L	L
	T	Acacia cultriformis	knife acacia	L	L	L	L	/	/
☆	T	Acacia dealbata	silver wattle	VL	L	L	L	/	/
☆	T	Acacia decurrens	green wattle	VL	L	L	L	/	/
	T	Acacia farnesiana	sweet acacia	?	?	L	L	/	L
	T S	Acacia greggii	catclaw acacia	L	L	L	L	L	L
☆	T S	Acacia longifolia	Sydney golden wattle	VL	L	L	L	/	/
☆	T	Acacia melanoxylon	blackwood acacia	L	L	M	M	/	L
	T	Acacia pendula	weeping acacia	?	?	VL	?	L	L
	T	Acacia pennatula	acacia (pennatula)	L	L	L	L	L	L
	S Gc	Acacia redolens	prostrate acacia	?	?	L	M	/	M
	T	Acacia salicina	willow acacia	L	L	L	L	/	M
	T S	Acacia saligna	blue leaf wattle	?	?	?	?	/	L
	T	Acacia schaffneri	twisted acacia	?	?	VL	L	/	L
	T	Acacia smallii	desert sweet acacia	?	L	L	L	/	L
	T	Acacia stenophyla	eumong/shoestring acacia	?	L	L	L	/	L
	T	Acacia willardiana	palo blanco	/	?	?	?	/	L
	P	Acanthus mollis	bear's breech	M	M	M	M	/	M
	T	Acer buergeranum	trident maple	M	M	M	/	/	/
	T S	Acer circinatum	vine maple	M	H	/	/	/	/
	T	Acer griseum	paperbark maple	M	M	?	?	?	?
	T	Acer macrophyllum	big leaf maple	M	H	M	H	/	/
	T	Acer negundo	box elder	M	M	M	M	/	/
	T	Acer oblongum	evergreen maple (oblongum)	M	/	M	M	/	/
	T	Acer palmatum	Japanese maple	M	M	H	H	/	/
	T	Acer paxii	evergreen maple (paxii)	M	M	M	M	/	/
	T	Acer platanoides	Norway maple	M	M	/	H	/	/
	T	Acer rubrum	scarlet red maple	M	H	H	H	/	/
	T	Acer saccharinum	silver maple	M	M	/	M	/	/
	T	Acer saccharum	sugar maple	M	/	/	/	/	/
	T	Acer truncatum	Chinese maple	M	M	/	H	/	/
	P	Achillea ageratifolia	Greek yarrow	L	M	M	M	M	M
	P	Achillea filipendulina	fern leaf yarrow	L	L	L	L	M	M
☆	P	Achillea millefolium	common yarrow	L	L	L	L	M	M
	Gc P	Achillea tomentosa	woolly yarrow	L	L	L	L	M	M
	P	Aconitum napellus	garden monkshood	M	/	/	/	/	/
	P	Acorus gramineus	sweet flag	H	H	H	H	H	H
	V	Actinidia deliciosa	kiwi	H	H	H	H	/	/
	S	Adenostoma fasciculatum	chamise	VL	VL	VL	VL	/	/
	T S	Adenostoma sparsifolium	red shanks/ribbonwood	VL	?	VL	VL	/	/
	P	Adiantum spp.	maidenhair fern	H	H	H	H	H	H
	S P	Aeonium spp.	Canary Island rose	L	/	L	L	/	L
	T	Aesculus californica	California buckeye	VL	VL	VL	L	/	/
	T	Aesculus carnea	red horsechestnut	M	M	M	/	/	/
	P	Agapanthus africanus	lily-of-the-Nile	M	M	M	M	/	M

General Plant Factors (estimated water needs) Compared to Reference ET (100%)

- **Turf** – High/Medium, Cool Season Turf – 80%-100% or (.8 - 1.0), Warm Season Turf – 60%-80% (.6 - .8)
- **Groundcovers** – Medium/ Medium High, – 50% - 80% or (.5 - .8)
- **Shrubs** – Medium/ Low, 50% or (.5)
- **Trees** – Medium/Low, 50% or (.5)
- **Natives** – Low, 50% or below (.5 and lower)
- **Annuals** – Medium/High, 60% – 100% or (.6 - 1.0)

Source: U.C. Cooperative Extension

TYPE	BOTANICAL NAME	COMMON NAME	1	2	3	4	5	6
			REGIONAL EVALUATIONS					
T	Agathis australis	Australian agathis/ kauri	M	/	M	/	/	/
T	Agathis robusta	Queensland kauri	M	/	M	H	/	/
S P	Agave spp.	agave	L	L	L	L	/	L
T	Agonis flexuosa	peppermint tree	L	/	L	M	/	/
✫ T	Ailanthus altissima	tree of heaven	VL	VL	L	L	L	L
Gc	Ajuga reptans	carpet bugle	M	M	M	H	H	H
V	Akebia quinata	fiveleaf akebia	M	M	M	M	/	/
✫ T	Albezia distachya	plume albizia	L	/	L	/	/	/
T	Albizia julibrissin	silk tree	L	L	M	M	M	M
T	Alectryon excelsus	alectryon/titoki	M	/	M	/	/	/
V	Allamanda cathartica	golden trumpet	/	/	M	/	/	/
T	Alnus cordata	Italian alder	M	M	M	M	/	/
T	Alnus glutinosa	black alder	M	M	M	H	/	/
T	Alnus oregona	Oregon alder	H	H	/	/	/	/
T	Alnus rhombifolia	white alder	H	H	H	H	H	/
P	Alocasia spp.	elephant's ear	H	H	H	H	/	/
T S	Aloe spp.	aloe	L	· L	L	L	/	L
P	Alopecurus pratensis 'Aureus'	golden foxtail	?	?	M	?	?	?
S	Aloysia machrostachya	aloysia	?	?	?	?	L	L
S P	Alpinia zerumbet	shell ginger	H	/	H	H	/	H
P	Alstroemeria spp.	Peruvian lily	M	M	M	M	?	M
S	Alyogyne hakeifolia	red centered hibiscus	/	/	L	L	/	/
S	Alyogyne huegelii	blue hibiscus	L	L	L	L	/	L
P	Amaryllis belladona	naked lady	VL	VL	VL	L	L	L
S	Ambrosia dumosa	white bursage	?	?	/	/	L	L
V	Ampelopis brevipedunculata	blueberry creeper	M	M	/	M	M	M
P	Anagallis monellii	pimpernel	?	?	M	/	/	/
S Gc	Andromeda polifolia	bog rosemary	H	H	/	/	/	/
P	Anemone X hybrida	Japanese anemone	M	M	M	M	M	M
V	Anemopaegma chamberlaynii	yellow trumpet vine	?	?	M	M	/	/
T	Angophora costata	gum myrtle	L	/	L	M	/	/
P	Anigozanthos flavidus	kangaroo paw	M	M	M	M	/	M
S	Anisacanthus spp.	desert honeysuckle	?	?	L	L	L	L
S	Anisodontea X hypomandarum	South African mallow	M	M	M	M	/	M
S	Anisodontea scabrosa	false mallow	M	M	M	M	/	M
T	Annona cherimola	cherimoya	M	/	M	/	/	/
Gc V	Antigonon leptopus	coral vine	M	/	M	M	/	M
Gc	Aptenia cordifolia	ice plant (Aptenia)	L	L	L	L	/	H
✱ GC	Aptenia 'Red Apple'	ice plant (Red Apple)	L	L	L	L	/	H
P	Aquilegia spp.	columbine	L	L	M	M	M	M
P	Arabis spp.	rockcress	L	M	M	?	?	?
T	Araucaria araucana	monkey puzzle tree	L	M	/	M	/	/
T	Araucaria bidwilii	bunya-bunya	L	M	M	M	/	/
T	Araucaria heterophyla	Norfolk Island pine	M	M	M	/	/	/
T	Arbutus 'Marina'	Marina arbutus	M	M	M	M	M	M
T	Arbutus menziesii	madrone	VL	VL	/	/	/	/
T S	Arbutus unedo	strawberry tree	L	L	L	L	M	M
T	Archontophoenix cunninghamiana	king palm	M	M	M	M	/	/
S Gc	Arctostaphylos cultivars	manzanita cultivars	L	L	L	L	/	/
S Gc	Arctostaphylos spp.	manzanita	VL	L	L	L	/	/
✫ Gc P	Arctotheca calendula	cape weed	M	M	M	M	/	M
P	Arctotis hybrids	African daisy	M	M	L	L	/	M
Gc	Ardisia japonica	Japanese ardesia, marlberry	M	/	H	/	/	/
T	Arecastrum romanzoffianum	queen palm	L	M	M	M	M	M
	Arenaria spp. (See Sagina)	Irish, Scotch moss						
P	Arenaria montana	sandwort	?	M	M	M	?	?
P	Aristea ecklonii	little Tyler	?	?	M	M	/	/
V	Aristolochia californica	California Dutchman's pipe	L	L	?	M	/	/

TYPE	BOTANICAL NAME	COMMON NAME	1	2	3	4	5	6
V	Aristolochia durior	Dutchman's pipe	M	M	?	M	/	/
V	Aristolochia elegans	calico flower	/	/	M	M	/	/
Gc P	Armeria maritima	sea pink	M	M	M	M		M
P	Arrenatherum eliatus bulbosum 'Vgta.'	bulb oat grass	?	?	M	?	M	M
S Gc	Artemisia spp. (shrubby)	sagebrush	VL	L	L	L	L	L
Gc P	Artemisia spp. (herbaceous)	tarragon/angel's hair etc.	L	L	L	L	M	M
P	Arthropodium cirrhatum	star lily	?	?	M	?	/	/
P	Arundo donax	giant reed	M	M	M	M	M	M
S	Arundinaria spp.	bamboo (Arundinaria)	L	L	M	M	/	M
Gc P	Asarum caudadum	wild ginger	M	M	H	?	/	/
P	Asparagus spp.	ornamental asparagus	M	M	M	M	/	M
P	Aspidistra elatior	cast iron plant	L	L	M	M	/	M
P	Asplenium bulbiferum	mother fern	H	H	H	H	/	/
P	Asplenium nidus	bird's nest fern	H	H	H	/	/	/
P	Astelia nervosa chathamica	silver spear	?	?	M	?	?	?
P	Aster spp.	aster	M	M	M	M	M	M
P	Asteriscus maritimus	gold coin, Canary Island daisy	M	M	L	M	/	/
P	Asteriscus sericeus	asteriscus	L	?	VL	/	/	/
P	Astilbe hybrids	false spirea	H	H	/	/	/	/
P	Athyrium filix-femina	lady fern	M	H	H	H	H	/
S Gc	Atriplex spp.	saltbush	VL	VL	VL	VL	/	VL
S	Aucuba japonica	Japanese aucuba	M	M	M	M	/	M
S	Azara dentata	orono	M	/	H	/	M	/
S	Azara microphylla	box leaf azara	M	/	H	/	M	/
P	Babiana stricta hybrids	baboon flower	L	L	L	?	/	/
S	Baccharis pilularis consanguinea	coyote brush	L	L	L	L	/	/
S Gc	Baccharis pilularis cvs.	dwarf coyote brush	L	L	L	L	/	/
S	Baccharis sarothroides	desert broom	VL	L	VL	L	L	L
S Gc	Baccharis 'Centennial'	bentennial baccharis	VL	L	VL	L	L	L
P	Baileya multiradiata	desert marigold	?	?	?	L	L	L
S	Bambusa spp.	bamboo (Bambusa)	L	L	M	M	M	M
T S	Banksia integrifolia	tree banksia	M	/	M	M	/	M
T S	Banksia speciosa	showy banksia	M	/	M	?	/	M
S	Barleria obtusa	barleria	?	?	M	M	/	/
T	Bauhinia blakeana	Hong Kong orchid tree	/	/	M	M	/	M
V	Bauhinia corymbosa	phanera	/	/	M	?	/	M
T	Bauhinia forficata	Brazilian butterfly tree	/	/	M	M	/	/
T S	Bauhinia punctata	red bauhinia	/	/	M	M	/	/
T	Bauhinia variegata	purple orchid tree	/	/	M	M	/	M
T S	Beaucarnea recurvata	bottle palm	/	/	L	L	/	L
V	Beaumontia grandiflora	Easter lily vine	M	/	M	H	/	/
P	Begonia 'Richmondensis'	Richmond begonia	M	M	M	M	/	M
P	Begonia semperflorens	begonia	M	M	M	M	/	M
Gc	Berberis irwinii	barberry	M	M	/	/	M	M
S GC	Berberis spp.	barberry	L	L	M	M	M	M
P	Bergenia cordifolia	heartleaf bergenia	M	M	M	H	H	H
P	Bergenia crassifolia	winter blooming bergenia	M	M	M	H	H	H
P	Berlandiera lyrata	chocolate scented daisy	?	M	?	?	M	M
P	Beschorneria yuccoides	Mexican lily	/	/	M	?	?	?
T	Betula fontinalis (see b. occidentalis)							
T	Betula jacquemontii	white barked Himalayan birch	H	H	/	/	/	/
T	Betula nigra	river/red birch	H	H	H	H	/	/
T	Betula occidentalis (fontinalis)	water birch	H	/	H	H	/	/
T	Betula pendula	European white birch	H	H	H	H	/	/
P	Billbergia spp.	queen's tears etc.	M	/	M	M	/	M
T	Bischofia javanica	toog	/	/	M	?	/	/
P	Blechnum occidentale	hammock fern	H	?	H	?	?	?
P	Bletilla striata	Chinese ground orchid	M	M	M	?	?	?

TYPE	BOTANICAL NAME	COMMON NAME	1	2	3	4	5	6
S	Boronia spp.	boronia	M	/	M	/	/	/
S Gc V	Bougainvillea spp.	bougainvillea	L	L	LL	L	/	M
T	Brachychiton acerifolius	flame tree	L	/	L	M	/	/
T	Brachychiton discolor	Queensland lace bark	M	/	L	M	/	/
T	Brachychiton X hybridus	hybrid brachychiton	M	/	M	M	/	M
T	Brachychiton populneus	bottle tree	L	M	L	L	M	M
T	Brachychiton rupestris	Queensland bottle tree	/	/	L	L	/	?
P	Brachycome multifida	Swan River daisy	M	M	M	M	M	M
T	Brahea armata	Mexican blue palm	L	/	L	L	L	L
T	Brahea edulis	Guadelupe palm	L	/	L	L	L	L
S	Brassaia actinophylla	Queensland umbrella tree	/	/	M	/	/	M
S	Breynia disticha	Hawaiian snow bush	?	?	H	H	/	/
☆ P	Briza media	quaking grass	L	?	M	M	M	M
P	Brodiaea spp.	brodiaea	VL	VL	L	L	/	/
S	Brugmansia spp.	angel's trumpet	M	/	M	H	/	/
S	Brunfelsia pauciflora	yesterday today and tomorrow	M	M	M	H	/	H
P	Brunnera macrophylla	Siberian bugloss	H	H	H	?	?	?
S	Buddleia alternifolia	fountain butterfly bush	L	L	M	/	M	M
S	Buddleia davidii	butterfly bush	L	L	M	M	M	M
S	Buddleia marrubiifolia	woolly butterfly bush	?	?	?	L	/	L
P	Bulbine frutescens	stalked bulbine	L	?	L	L	/	L
T	Bursera hindsiana	bursera	?	?	/	/	/	M
T	Butia capitata	pindo palm	L	L	L	L	L	L
S	Buxus microphylla japonica	Japanese boxwood	M	M	M	M	M	M
S	Buxus sempervirens	English boxwood	M	M	M	/	M	M
S	Caesalpinea cacalaco	cascalote	?	?	?	?	/	L
S	Caesalpinea gilliesii	desert bird of paradise	L	L	L	L	M	M
S	Caesalpinea mexicana	Mexican bird of paradise	?	/	?	L	/	L
S	Caesalpinea pulcherrima	dwarf poinciana	L	L	M	M	/	M
P	Calamagrostis spp.	feather reed	?	?	M	M	/	?
S	Calliandra californica	Baja fairy duster	/	/	VL	L	/	L
S	Calliandra eriophylla	fairy duster	/	/	VL	VL	/	L
S	Calliandra haematocephala	pink powder puff	/	/	M	M	/	H
S	Calliandra tweedii	trinidad flame bush	/	/	M	M	/	M
S	Callicarpa dichotoma	lavender beautyberry	M	?	M	?	?	?
S	Callicarpa japonica	beauty berry	/	M	/	M	/	/
T S	Callistemon citrinus	bottle brush	L	L	L	L	/	M
T S	Callistemon pinifolius	pine-leafed bottlebrush	?	?	L	?	?	?
T S	Callistemon salignus	pink tips/white bottlebrush	L	M	M	?	/	?
T S	Callistemon speciosus	Albany bottlebrush	?	?	M	?	/	M
T S	Callistemon viminalis	weeping bottle brush	L	L	M	M	/	M
S	Calluna vulgaris	Scotch heather	M	M	/	/	/	/
T	Calocedrus decurrens	incense cedar	M	M	M	M	M	/
S	Calocephalus brownii	cushion bush	L	/	L	L	/	L
T	Calodendrum capense	cape chestnut	L	/	M	M	/	/
S	Calothamnus quadrifidus	net bush	?	?	M	?	/	?
S	Calycanthus occidentalis	western spice bush	L	M	M	M	/	/
Gc	Calyophus hartwegii	Sierra sundrop	?	?	?	?	?	M
S	Camellia japonica	camellia	M	M	M	H	/	H
S	Camellia sasanqua	sasanqua camellia	M	M	M	H	/	H
Gc	Campanula poscharskyana	Serbian bell flower	M	M	M	M	/	M
P	Campanula spp.	bell flower	M	M	M	M	/	M
V	Campsis spp.	trumpet creeper	L	L	M	M	M	M
P	Canna spp.	canna	M	M	M	H	M	M
S	Capparis spinosa	caper bush	L	/	L	?	?	?
P	Carex (garden spp.)	sedge	M	M	M	M	/	M
Gc	Carissa macrocarpa (prost.cvs.)	Natal plum	L	/	M	M	/	M
S	Carissa spp.	Natal plum	L	/	M	M	/	M
S	Carnegiea gigantea	saguaro	/	/	VL	L	/	L

TYPE	BOTANICAL NAME	COMMON NAME	1	2	3	4	5	6
S	Carpenteria californica	bush anemone	L	L	L	M	/	/
T	Carpinus betulus 'Fastigiata'	European hornbeam	L	M	/	/	/	/
★ Gc	Carpobrotus spp.	ice plant (Carpobrotus)	L	M	VL	L	/	L
T	Carya illinoensis	pecan	L	M	M	M	M	M
S P	Caryopteris X clandonensis	blue mist	M	M	M	M	/	/
T	Caryota mitis	clustered fishtail palm	/	/	M	/	/	/
T S	Caryota urens	fishtail wine palm	H	/	M	/	/	/
T S	Caryota urens	hardy fishtail wine palm	H	/	M	H	/	/
T	Casimiroa edulis	white sapote	M	/	M	M	/	/
S	Cassia artemisioides	feathery cassia	L	L	L	L	L	L
S	Cassia bicapsularis (C.candolleana)	New Zealand cassia	?	L	L	/	/	L
S	Cassia eremophila (C.nemophila)	desert cassia	/	?	L	L	L	L
T	Cassia leptophylla	gold medallion tree	L	L	M	M	/	/
S	Cassia odorata	cassia (odorata)	?	?	L	L	/	L
S	Cassia phyllodenia	silver cassia	?	?	L	L	L	L
T	Cassia spectabilis (C.excelsa)	crown of gold tree	L	/	M	M	/	/
S	Cassia sturtii	Sturt's cassia	/	/	L	/	/	L
S	Cassia tomentosa	wooly senna	VL	/	L	?	/	M
S	Cassia wizlizeni	shrubby cassia	?	?	L	?	/	L
T	Castanospermum australe	Moreton Bay chestnut	L	/	M	M	/	/
T	Casuarina cunninghamiana	river she-oak	L	L	L	L	M	M
T	Casuarina stricta	coast beefwood	L	L	L	L	M	M
T	Catalpa speciosa	western catalpa	L	M	M	M	M	M
P	Catananche caerulea	cupid's dart	?	L	M	?	?	?
P	Catharanthus roseus	Madagascar periwinkle	M	M	M	M	M	M
S Gc	Ceanothus spp.	California lilac	VL	L	VL	L	/	/
S Gc	Ceanothus cultivars	ceanothus	L	L	L	L	/	/
T	Cedrus atlantica	Atlas cedar	M	M	L	M	M	M
T	Cedrus deodora	deodar cedar	L	M	L	M	M	M
T	Celtis australis	European hackberry	L	M	/	/	M	M
T	Celtis occidentalis	common Hackberry	L	L	/	M	M	M
T	Celtis reticulata	western hackberry	L	/	/	/	L	L
T	Celtis sinensis	Chinese hackberry	L	M	/	M	M	M
P	Centaurea cineraria	dusty miller (cineraria)	L	L	M	M	/	M
P	Centaurea gymnocarpa	velvet centaurea	L	L	M	M	/	M
☆ P	Centranthus ruber	red valerian	VL	VL	L	L	/	M
S	Cephalocereus spp.	old man cactus	/	/	VL	L	L	L
Gc	Cephalophyllum spp.	ice plant (Cephalophyllum)	L	L	L	L	/	L
Gc	Cerastium tomentosum	snow in summer	M	M	M	M	M	M
T	Ceratonia siliqua	carob	L	/	M	M	M	M
S	Ceratostigma abyssinica	African plumbago	L	M	M	M	M	M
S	Ceratostigma griffithii	Burmese plumbago	L	M	M	M	M	M
Gc	Ceratostigma plumbaginoides	dwarf plumbago	L	M	M	M	M	M
T	Cercidium floridum	blue palo verde	VL	VL	VL	L	/	L
T	Cercidium microphyllum	little leaf palo verde	/	VL	VL	L	/	L
T	Cercidium praecox	Sonoran palo verde	/	L	VL	L	/	L
T	Cercidium 'Sonorae'	Sonora cercidium	?	?	?	?	/	L
T	Cercis canadensis	eastern redbud	M	M	M	M	/	/
T S	Cercis occidentalis	western redbud	VL	VL	L	L	/	/
T	Cercis reniformis	southwest redbud	L	L	?	?	?	?
S	Cercocarpus betuloides	mountain ironwood	VL	VL	VL	VL	VL	
S	Cercocarpus minutiflorus	San Diego mountain mahogany	L	?	VL	VL	/	
S	Cereus peruvianus	Peruvian apple cactus	?	?	L	L	/	L
S	Cestrum elegans	red cestrum	M	/	M	M	/	M
S	Cestrum nocturnum	night jessamine	M	M	M	M	/	M
S	Chaenomeles cvs.	flowering quince	L	L	M	M	M	M
T S	Chamaecyparis spp.	false cypress	M	M	/	/	/	/
S P	Chamaedorea spp.	chamaedorea	/	/	H	H	/	H
Gc P	Chamaemelum nobile	chamomile	L	M	M	M	M	M

General Plant Factors (estimated water needs) Compared to Reference ET (100%)

- **Turf** – High/Medium, Cool Season Turf – 80%-100% or (.8 - 1.0), Warm Season Turf – 60%-80% (.6 - .8)
- **Groundcovers** – Medium/ Medium High, – 50% - 80% or (.5 -.8)
- **Shrubs** – Medium/ Low, 50% or (.5)
- **Trees** – Medium/Low, 50% or (.5)
- **Natives** – Low, 50% or below (.5 and lower)
- **Annuals** – Medium/High, 60% – 100% or (.6 - 1.0)

Source: U.C. Cooperative Extension

TYPE	BOTANICAL NAME	COMMON NAME	REGIONAL EVALUATIONS					
			1	2	3	4	5	6
T S	Chamaerops humilis	Mediterranean fan palm	L	L	M	M	M	M
S	Chamelaucium uncinatum	Geraldton wax flower	L	L	L	M	/	M
P	Chasmanthium latifolium	sea oats	M	M	M	M	M	M
P	Cheiranthus cheiri	wall flower	M	M	M	M	M	M
T	Chilopsis linearis	desert willow	VL	VL	VL	L	M	M
T	Chionanthus retusus	Chinese fringe tree	M	M	M	M	/	/
T	Chitalpa tashkentensis	chitalpa	L	M	L	L	L	M
S	Choisya ternata	Mexican orange	M	M	M	M	/	M
P	Chondropetalum tectorum	cape reed	?	?	M	?	?	?
T	Chorisia insignis	white floss silk tree	M	/	M	L	/	M
T	Chorisia speciosa	floss silk tree	L	/	L	L	/	M
P	Chrysanthemum frutescens	marguerite daisy	M	M	M	M	/	M
P	Chrysanthemum maximum	Shasta daisy	M	M	M	M	M	M
P	Chrysanthemum parthenium	feverfew	L	L	M	M	M	M
P	Cibotium glaucum	Hawaiian tree fern	?	/	H	H	/	/
T	Cinnamomum camphora	camphor tree	M	M	M	M	/	M
V	Cissus antarctica	kangaroo treebine	L	M	M	M	/	M
V	Cissus rhombifolia	grape ivy	/	M	M	M	/	M
S Gc	Cistus spp.	rockrose	L	L	L	L	L	L
T S	Citrus spp.	orange, lemon etc.	M	M	M	M	/	M
V	Clematis armandii	evergreen clematis	M	M	M	M	M	M
V	Clematis hybrids	deciduous clematis	M	M	H	H	M	M
V	Clematis lasiantha	pipestem clematis	L	L	VL	L	/	/
V	Clematis ligusticifolia	western virgin's bower	M	?	?	L	/	/
V	Clematis pauciflora	small flowered clematis	?	?	VL	L	?	?
S	Cleome isomeris	bladder Pod	VL	VL	VL	VL	L	L
P	Clerodendrum bungei	cashmere bouquet	L	M	M	?	?	?
S	Clerodendrum ugandense	glory bower	/	?	M	M	/	M
P	Clivia miniata	kaffir lily	M	M	L	M	/	M
V	Clytostoma callistigioides	violet trumpet vine	M	M	M	M	/	M
T S	Cocculus laurifolius	laurel leaf cocculus	M	M	M	M	/	M
S	Coleonema album	white breath of heaven	M	M	M	M	/	/
S	Coleonema pulchrum	breath of heaven	M	M	M	M	/	/
S T	Comarostaphylis diversifolia	summer holly	VL	L	VL	L	/	/
V	Combretum fruticosum	combretum	/	/	M	M	/	/
S	Convolvulus cneorum	bush morning glory	L	L	L	L	L	L
Gc P	Convolvulus mauritanicus	ground morning glory	L	L	L	L	M	M
S Gc	Coprosma kirkii	creeping coprosma	L	L	M	M	/	/
S Gc	Coprosma pumila 'Verde Vista'	verde vista coprosma	L	L	M	M	/	/
✿ S	Coprosma repens	mirror plant	M	M	M	M	/	/
T S	Cordia boissieri	Texas olive	?	?	?	L	L	L
S	Cordia parvifolia	little leaf cordia	?	?	?	L	L	L
✿ T	Cordyline australis	New Zealand cabbage tree	L	M	L	M	M	M
S	Cordyline stricta	palm lily	/	M	M	M	/	M
P	Coreopsis auriculata 'Nana'	dwarf coreopsis	L	L	L	L	M	M
P	Coreopsis lanceolata	coreopsis	L	L	L	L	M	M
P	Coreopsis verticilata cvs.	threadleaf coreopsis	L	L	L	L	M	M
P	Corethrogyne californica	black bush	?	?	/	/	VL	/
T	Cornus florida	eastern dogwood	H	H	H	/	/	/
T	Cornus nuttallii	western dogwood	M	M	/	M	/	/
S	Cornus stolonifera	redtwig dogwood	H	H	/	H	/	/
S	Corokia cotoneaster	wire-netting bush	M	M	M	M	M	M
S	Correa spp.	Australian fuchsia	L	L	L	L	/	M
★ S	Cortaderia sellowana cvs.	pampas grass	VL	L	L	L	L	L
T S	Corylus maxima	filbert	L	/	/	/	/	/
S	Corylus avelleana contorta	Harry Lauder's walking stick	M	M	/	/	/	/
S	Corylus cornuta californica	western hazelnut	L	?	/	/	/	/
T	Corynocarpus laevigata	New Zealand laurel	M	/	H	/	/	/
T S	Cotinus coggygria	smoke tree	L	L	L	L	L	/

	TYPE	BOTANICAL NAME	COMMON NAME	REGIONAL EVALUATIONS					
				1	2	3	4	5	6
★	S	Cotoneaster spp. (shrubs)	cotoneaster	L	L	L	M	M	M
★	Gc	Cotoneaster spp.(ground covers)	cotoneaster	M	M	M	M	M	M
	P	Cotula lineariloba	silver button plant	?	?	M	?	?	?
	S P	Cotyledon spp.	cotyledon	L	L	L	L	/	L
	S	Coursetia axillaris	baby bonnets	?	?	?	?	?	L
	S	Cowania mexicana	cliff rose	L	?	/	L	L	L
	S P	Crassula spp.	crassula	L	L	L	L	/	L
☆	T	Crataegus spp.	hawthorne	M	M	/	M	M	/
	T	Crinodendron patagua	lily-of-the-valley tree	M	/	M	?	/	/
	P	Crinum spp.	crinum lily, spider lily	M	?	M	M	?	M
	P	Crocrosmia hybrids (Tritonia)	montbrieta	L	L	L	L	/L	
	S	Crotalaria agatiflora	canary-bird bush	L	/	M	M	/	H
	T S	Cryptomeria japonica	Japanese cryptomeria	M	H	H	H	/	H
	T	Cupaniopsis anacardioides	carrotwood	M	/	M	M	/	M
	P	Cuphea hyssophyla	false heather	M	M	M	M	/	M
	P	Cuphea ignea	cigar plant	M	M	M	M	/	/
	P Gc	Cuphea llavea	bat-faced cuphea	?	?	?	?	/	M
	S P	Cuphea micropetela	cuphea (micropetala)	?	?	M	?	/	?
	T	X Cupressocyparis leylandii	Leyland cypress	M	M	M	/	M	M
	T	Cupressus arizonica var.glabra	smooth Arizona cypress	VL	VL	VL	L	L	L
	T	Cupressus guadalupensis forbesii	tecate cypress	L	L	VL	VL	/	/
☆	T	Cupressus macrocarpa	Monterey cypress	M	M	M	/	/	/
	T	Cupressus sempervirens	Italian cypress	L	L	L	L	M	M
	T	Cussonia paniculata	little cabbage tree	/	/	M	?	/	?
	S P	Cyathea cooperii	Australian tree fern	H	H	H	H	/	/
	S	Cycas revoluta	sago palm	M	M	M	M	M	M
	P	Cyclamen hederifolium	cyclamen	L	L	M	?	/	M
	P	Cyclamen persicum hybrids	florists' cyclamen	M	M	M	M	/	M
	Gc P	Cymbalaria muralis	Kenilworth ivy	M	M	H	H	/	/
	P	Cyperus alternifolius	umbrella Plant	H	H	H	H	H	H
	P	Cyrtonium falcatum	holly fern	M	M	H	M	/	M
	Gc	Cytissus kewensis	Kew broom	M	M	/	/	M	/
★	S	Cytisus spp.	broom (Cytisus)	L	L	/	M	/	/
	S	Daboecia cantabrica	Irish heath	M	?	?	?	/	/
	S	Dahlia imperialis	tree dahlia	M	M	M	M	/	?
	P	Dahlia spp.	dahlia	M	M	M	H	H	H
	T	Dalbergia sissoo	sissoo	/	/	/	/	/	M
	S	Dalea bicolor	dalea (bicolor)	/	/	L	L	/	M
	Gc	Dalea capitata	dalea (capitata)	/	/	?	?	M	M
	S	Dalea frutescens	black dalea	/	/	M	/	M	M
	Gc	Dalea greggii	trailing indigo bush	?	/	L	L	L	L
	S	Dalea lutea	dalea (lutea)	/	/	/	?	M	M
	Gc	Dalea orcutii	Baja indigo bush	/	/	L	L	/	L
	S	Dalea pulchra	indigo/pea bush	/	/	M	/	M	M
	T	Dalea spinosa	smoke tree	/	L	/	L	L	L
	S	Dalea versicolor	dalea (versicolor)	/	/	M	/	M	M
	S	Daphne odora	winter daphne	M	M	/	/	M	M
	S	Dasylirion spp.	desert spoon	?	?	L	L	L	L
	P	Davallia trichomanoides	squirrel's foot fern	M	H	M	H	/	H
☆	Gc	Delosperma spp.	ice plant (Delosperma)	L	M	L	L	/	L
	P	Delphinium spp.	delphinium	M	M	M	M	M	M
	T S	Dendriopoterium menendezii	dendriopoterium	?	?	M	?	/	?
	S	Dendromecon spp.	bush poppy	VL	L	VL	L	/	/
	P	Deschampsia caespitosa	tufted hairgrass	L	L	L	L	/	/
	S	Deutzia spp.	bridal wreath	M	M	/	M	M	/
	P	Dianella tasmanica	blueberry	M	?	M	M	/	?
	P	Dianthus spp.	pink/carnation	M	M	M	M	M	M
	P	Diascia spp.	twinspur	M	M	M	M	/	/
	P	Dicentra spp.	bleeding heart	M	M	M	H	/	/

General Plant Factors (estimated water needs) Compared to Reference ET (100%)

- **Turf –** High/Medium, Cool Season Turf – 80%-100% or (.8 - 1.0), Warm Season Turf – 60%-80% (.6 - .8)
- **Groundcovers –** Medium/ Medium High, – 50% - 80% or (.5 - .8)
- **Shrubs –** Medium/ Low, 50% or (.5)
- **Trees –** Medium/Low, 50% or (.5)
- **Natives –** Low, 50% or below (.5 and lower)
- **Annuals –** Medium/High, 60% – 100% or (.6 - 1.0)

Source: U.C. Cooperative Extension

TYPE	BOTANICAL NAME	COMMON NAME	REGIONAL EVALUATIONS					
			1	2	3	4	5	6
Gc	Dichondra micrantha	dichondra	H	H	H	H	/	H
S P	Dicksonia antarctica	Tasmanian tree fern	H	H	H	H	/	/
P	Dicliptera suberecta	velvet honeysuckle	L	?	M	?	?	M
P	Dierama spp.	fairy wand	M	M	M	?	?	?
P	Dietes bicolor	fortnight lily	L	L	M	M	/	M
P	Dietes vegeta	fortnight Lily	L	L	M	M	/	M
P	Digitalis mertonensis	foxglove	M	M	M	M	M	M
T	Diospyros kaki	Japanese persimmon	L	M	M	M	M	M
	Diplacus (see Mimulus)							
V	Distictis buccinatoria	blood red trumpet vine	M	M	M	M	/	M
V	Distictis 'Rivers'	royal trumpet vine	M	M	M	M	/	M
S	Dizygotheca elegantissima	thread leaf false aralia	/	M	M	M	/	M
S	Dodonaea viscosa	hopseed bush	L	L	L	M	/	M
S	Dodonaea viscosa 'Purpurea'	purple hopseed bush	L	L	L	M	/	M
T S	Dombeya spp.	dombeya	/	/	M	M	/	/
T	Dombeya cacuminum	strawberry snowball	?	/	M	M	/	/
S	Doryanthes palmeri	spear lily	L	/	L	L	/	/
S	Dorycnium hirsutum	dorycnium	/	?	L	?	?	?
T	Dracaena draco	dragon Tree	L	/	VL	L	/	/
Gc	Drosanthemum spp.	ice plant (Drosanthemum)	L	L	L	L	/	L
P	Dryopteris erythrosora	wood fern	M	M	M	M	/	/
☼ Gc	Duchesnea indica	Indian mock strawberry	M	M	M	M	/	M
P	Dudleya spp.	dudleya, live forever	L	L	VL	L	L	L
S	Duranta repens	sky flower	/	/	M	M	/	M
S	Duranta stenostachya	Brazilian sky flower	/	/	M	M	/	/
P	Dyckia spp.	dyckia	L	?	L	L	?	?
P Gc	Dymondia margaretae	dymondia	L	?	L	L	/	/
P	Dyssodia pentachaeta	golden fleece	?	M	?	?	M	M
S P	Echeveria spp.	hens and chickens	L	L	L	L	/	M
P	Echinacea spp.	cone flower	M	M	M	M	M	M
S	Echinocactus spp.	barrel cactus	VL	VL	L	L	/	L
P	Echinops exaltus	globe thistle	M	M	M	?	?	M
☼ S P	Echium fastuosum	pride of madeira	L	L	L	L	/	M
T S	Elaeagnus angustifolia	Russian olive	L	L	L	L	M	M
S	Eleagnus X ebbengei	Ebbinge's silverberry	L	L	?	?	M	M
S	Elaeagnus pungens	silverberry	L	L	L	L	L	L
P	Elymus spp.	wild rye	L	L	L	L	M	M
P	Encelia californica	California encelia	L	?	VL	L	/	L
S	Encelia farinosa	brittle bush	L	?	VL	L	L	L
S	Enkianthus campanulatus	red-veined enkianthus	M	H	?	?	?	?
S P	Ensete ventricosum	Abyssinian banana	H	H	H	H	/	H
P	Epilobium spp.(Zauchneria)	California fuchsia	L	L	VL	L	/	M
Gc	Epimedium grandiflorum	bishop's hat	M	M	/	/	/	/
P	Equisetum spp.	horsetail	H	H	H	H	H	H
S	Eremophila glabra	emu bush	L	?	L	?	/	L
S	Eremophila maculata	spotted emu bush	L	L	L	?	/	L
S Gc	Erica spp.	heath	M	M	M	/	/	/
S	Ericameria laricifolia (Haplopappus)	turpentine bush	?	?	?	?	L	L
P	Erigeron glaucus	beach aster	L	/	M	?	/	/
P	Erigeron karvinskianus	fleabane	L	M	M	M	M	M
S P	Eriogonum spp.	buckwheat	L	L	VL	L	L	L
P Gc	Erodium chamaedryoides	cranesbill(chamaedroides)	L	M	M	M	M	M
P Gc	Erodium chrysanthum	cranessbill (chrysanthum)	L	M	M	M	M	M
T	Eryobotrya deflexa	bronze loquat	M	M	M	M	/	M
T	Eryobotrya japonica	loquat	L	L	M	M	/	M
P	Erysimum linifolium	wallflower	L	L	L	M	/	M
T	Erythrina americana(E.coralloides)	naked coral tree	/	/	L	M	/	/
T	Erythrina caffra	kaffir bloom coral tree	/	/	L	L	/	/

	TYPE	BOTANICAL NAME	COMMON NAME	REGIONAL EVALUATIONS					
				1	2	3	4	5	6
	T S	Erythrina crista-galli	cockspur coral tree	M	M	L	L	/	M
	T	Erythrina falcata	coral tree (falcata)	/	/	L	/	/	/
	T	Erythrina humeana	Natal coral tree	/	M	L	M	/	/
	T	Erythrina sykesii	Sykes coral tree	?	/	L	L	/	/
	S	Escallonia spp.	escallonia	M	M	M	M	/	M
	P	Eschscholzia californica	California poppy	VL	L	L	L	L	L
	S	Espostoa lantana	Peruvian old man cactus	?	?	L	L	L	L
☆	T	Eucalyptus camaldulensis	red gum	VL	L	L	L	M	M
	T	Eucalyptus campaspe	silver gimlet	?	?	M	?	/	M
	T	Eucalyptus cinerea	ash leaved gum, silver dollar tree	VL	L	L	L	/	/
	T	Eucalyptus citriodora	lemon scented gum	L	/	L	M	/	M
	T	Eucalyptus cladocalyx	sugar gum	L	/	L	L	/	/
	T	Eucalyptus deglupta	mindinao gum	/	/	M	M	/	/
	T	Eucalyptus erythrocorys	red cap gum	L	L	M	M	/	M
	T	Eucalyptus ficifolia	red flowering gum	L	/	M	M	/	/
	T	Eucalyptus formanii	Forman's mallee	?	?	L	?	?	L
★	T	Eucalyptus globulus	blue gum	L	L	L	M	/	/
	T	Eucalyptus gunnii	cider gum	L	L	L	L	?	/
	T	Eucalyptus kruseana	book-leaf mallee	VL	/	L	?	/	?
	T	Eucalyptus lehmannii	bushy yate	L	L	L	L	/	/
	T	Eucalyptus leucoxylon	white ironbark	L	L	L	L	/	M
	T	Eucalyptus loxophleba	York gum	?	VL	?	VL	/	/
	T	Eucalyptus macranda	long flowered marlock	VL	VL	VL	L	/	L
	T	Eucalyptus maculata	spotted gum	L	/	M	M	/	/
	T	Eucalyptus microtheca	coolibah	L	L	L	L	M	M
	T	Eucalyptus nicholii	Nichol's willow leaf peppermint	L	L	M	M	M	M
	T	Eucalyptus polyanthemos	silver dollar gum	L	L	L	L	M	M
☆	T	Eucalyptus pulverulenta	silver mountain gum	L	M	M	M	/	M
	T	Eucalyptus robusta	swamp mahogany	L	L	L	L	/	/
	T	Eucalyptus rudis	flooded gum	L	L	L	L	M	M
	T	Eucalyptus sargentii	Salt River mallet	?	VL	?	L	/	L
	T	Eucalyptus sideroxylon	red iron bark	L	L	L	L	M	M
	T	Eucalyptus spathulata	swamp mallee	L	/	L	L	/	M
	T	Eucalyptus torelliana	cadaga	M	/	?	?	?	?
	T	Eucalyptus torquata	coral gum	L	L	L	M	/	M
	T	Eucalyptus viminalis	manna gum	L	L	L	M	/	M
	T	Eucalyptus woodwardii	lemon flowered gum	VL	?	L	?	?	L
	Gc	Euonymus fortunei	purple winter creeper	M	M	M	M	M	/
	V	Euonymus fortunei radicans	winter creeper	M	M	/	M	M	M
	S	Euonymus japonica	evergreen euonymus	L	L	M	M	M	M
	T S	Euphorbia cotinifolia	Carribean copper plant	/	/	M	/	/	/
	S	Euphorbia milii	crown of thorns	/	L	L	L	/	L
	S	Euphorbia pulcherrima	poinsettia	/	/	L	M	/	M
	S	Euphorbia rigida	euphorbia (rigida)	/	L	VL	L	/	L
	S	Euphorbia tirucali	milk bush	/	/	VL	/	/	L
	S P	Euryops pectinatus	euryops/shrub daisy	L	L	L	L	M	M
	S P	Euryops pectinatus viridis	green euryops	M	M	M	M	M	M
	P	Evolvulus nuttallianus	evolvulus	?	?	M	M	/	?
	S	Fabiana imbricana	fabiana	?	?	M	?	?	?
	T	Fagus sylvatica	European beech	M	H	/	/	/	/
	S	Fallugia paradoxa	Apache plume	/	?	VL	VL	L	L
	V	Fatshedera lizei	fatshedera	M	M	M	H	/	H
	S	Fatsia japonica	Japanese aralia	M	M	M	M	/	H
	T S	Feijoa sellowiana	pineapple guava	L	L	L	M	/	M
	S	Felicia amelloides	blue marguerite	M	M	M	M	/	M
	S	Felicia fruticosa	shrub aster	/	L	L	M	/	M
	S	Ferocactus spp.	barrel cactus	VL	VL	VL	L	L	L
	P	Festuca californica	California fescue	L	M	M	M	M	M

TYPE	BOTANICAL NAME	COMMON NAME	REGIONAL EVALUATIONS					
			1	2	3	4	5	6
P	Festuca ovina glauca	blue fescue	L	L	M	M	M	M
T	Ficus auriculata	Roxburgh fig	/	/	M	M	/	/
T S	Ficus benjamina	weeping Chinese banyan	/	/	M	/	/	M
T	Ficus carica	edible fig	M	M	M	M	M	M
T S	Ficus elastica	rubber plant	/	/	M	M	/	/
T	Ficus macrophylla	Moreton Bay fig	/	/	M	M	/	/
T	Ficus microcarpa	Indian laurel fig/ laurel fig	M	/	M	M	/	M
V	Ficus pumila	creeping fig	M	M	M	M	M	M
T	Ficus rubiginosa	rusty leaf fig	M	/	M	M	/	/
S	Forestiera neomexicana	desert olive	?	?	L	L	L	L
S	Forsythia X intermedia	forsythia	L	L	M	M	M	M
S	Fouquieria splendens	ocotillo	/	/	VL	L	L	L
Gc	Fragaria chiloensis	wild strawberry	M	M	M	M	M	M
P	Francoa ramosa	bridal wreath	M	M	M	?	?	?
T S	Franklinia alatamaha (Gordonia altmahama)	franklin tree	M	/	/	/	/	/
T	Fraxinus americana	white ash	M	M	/	/	/	/
T	Fraxinus latifolia	Oregon ash	H	H	/	/	/	/
T	Fraxinus 'Moraine'	moraine ash	M	M	/	M	M	
T	Fraxinus oxycarpa 'Raywood'	raywood ash	M	M	M	M	M	M
T	Fraxinus pennsylvanica 'Marshal'	green ash	M	M	/	/	M	M
T	Fraxinus uhdei	evergreen ash	M	M	M	M	H	H
T	Fraxinus velutina	Arizona ash	M	M	M	M	M	M
T	Fraxinus velutina 'Modesto'	Modesto ash	M	M	M	M	M	M
S	Fremontodendron spp.	flannel bush	VL	VL	VL	L	/	/
P	Fuchsia spp.	fuchsia	M	M	H	H	/	/
S	Furcraea spp.	furcraea	L	/	L	L	?	
P	Gaillardia grandiflora	blanket flower	L	L	M	M	M	M
P	Galium odoratum	sweet woodruff	M	M	H	/	/	/
S	Galvesia juncea	Baja bush-snapdragon	?	?	VL	L	/	M
S	Galvesia speciosa	island bush snapdragon	L	L	VL	L	?	M
S	Gamolepis chrysanthemumoides	gamolepis	M	M	M	M	/	H
S	Gardenia spp.	gardenia	M	M	M	M	/	M
S	Garrya eliptica	coast silktassel	L	L	L	M	/	/
S	Garrya flavescens	ashy silktassel	/	?	L	L	/	/
S	Garrya fremontii	Fremont silktassel	L	L	VL	/	/	/
P	Gasteria spp.	mother-in-law's tongue etc.	L	L	L	L	/	?
S	Gaultheria shallon	salal	M	M	/	H	/	/
P	Gaura lindheimeri	gaura	M	M	M	M	M	M
Gc	Gazania spp.	gazania	M	M	M	M	M	M
T	Geijera parviflora	Australian willow	M	M	L	M	M	M
V	Gelsemium sempervirens	Carolina jessamine	L	L	M	M	/	M
Gc	Genista lydia	Lydia woadwaxen	M	?	M	?	/	/
Gc	Genista pilosa (Vancouver Gold)	Vancouver gold genista	M	M	/	M	?	M
S	Genista spp.	broom (Genista)	L	L	M	M	/	M
Gc P	Geranium incanum	cranesbill (incanum)	L	L	M	M	/	M
P	Geranium sanguinium	cranesbill (sanguinium)	M	M	M	M	/	M
P	Gerbera jamesonii	Transvaal daisy	M	M	M	M	/	M
P	Geum spp.	geum	M	M	M	M	M	/
T	Ginkgo biloba	maiden hair tree	M	M	M	M	M	/
P Gc	Glechoma hederaceae	ground ivy	L	M	H	H	/	/
T	Gleditsia triacanthos	honey locust	L	L	M	L	L	L
T	Gordonia lasianthus	lob lolly bay	?	?	H	?	?	?
P	Graptopetalum spp.	graptopetalum	L	L	L	L	/	M
S	Grevillea spp.	grevillea	L	L	L	L	/	M
T	Grevillea robusta	silk oak	L	L	L	M	/	M
S	Grewia occidentalis	lavender star flower	M	M	M	M	/	M
S	Griselinia littoralis	griselinia (littoralis)	M	/	M	/	/	/

65

TYPE	BOTANICAL NAME	COMMON NAME	1	2	3	4	5	6
S	Griselinia lucida	griselinia (lucida)	M	/	M	/	/	/
S	Gutterrezia sarothrae	stickle Broom	?	?	/	/	L	L
P	Gypsophila paniculata	baby's breath	L	L	M	M	/	M
S	Hakea laurina	sea urchin tree	L	L	L	L	/	/
S	Hakea suaveolens	sweet hakea	L	L	L	L	/	/
S	Hamamelis virginiana	common witch hazel	M	M	/	/	/	/
S	Hamelia patens	Texas firecracker bush	?	?	?	?	/	M
V	Hardenbergia violacea	lilac vine	M	M	M	M	/	M
T	Harpephyllum caffrum	kaffir plum	M	/	M	M	/	/
T	Harpullia arborea	tulipwood	/	/	M	/	/	/
P	Haworthia spp.	haworthia	L	L	L	L	/	L
S	Hebe spp.	hebe	M	M	M	M	/	/
☆ Gc V	Hedera canariensis	Algerian ivy	M	M	M	M	M	M
★ Gc V	Hedera helix	English ivy	M	M	M	M	M	M
S	Hedychium coronarium	white ginger lily	M	/	H	H	/	H
S	Hedychium gardneranum	Kahili ginger	M	/	H	H	/	H
P	Helianthemum nummularium	sunrose	L	L	L	L	/	/
P	Helictotrichon sempervirens	blue oat grass	L	L	M	M	M	M
P	Heliotrropum arborescens	common heliotrope	M	M	M	?	?	M
P	Helleborus spp.	hellebore	M	M	M	M	/	/
P	Hemerocallis spp.	day ily	M	M	M	M	M	M
Gc	Herniaria glabra	green carpet	H	M	M	/	/	
S	Hesperaloe funifera	Coahuilan hesperaloe	?	?	VL	L	L	L
S	Hesperaloe parviflora	red/ yellow yucca	?	?	VL	L	L	L
S	Heteromeles arbutifolia	toyon	VL	VL	L	L	/	/
P	Heuchera maxima	island alum root	M	/	M	M	/	/
P	Heuchera sanguinea	coral bells	M	M	M	M	M	M
P	Hibbertia cuniformis	hibbertia	M	M	/	/	/	M
V	Hibbertia scandens	Guinea gold vine	M	M	M	M	/	M
S	Hibiscus rosa-sinensis	Chinese hibiscus	M	M	M	M	/	H
S P	Hibiscus mutabilis	confederate rose	M	M	?	M	?	?
S	Hibiscus syriacus	rose of Sharon	L	M	M	M	M	M
P	Hosta spp.	plantain lily	M	M	/	/	/	/
P	Houttuynia cordata 'Chameleon'	chameleon houttuynia	M	M	M	?	?	?
S	Howea forsterana	sentry palm	/	/	M	M	/	/
S V	Hydrangea anomala petiolaris	climbing hydrangea	M	H	/	H	/	/
S	Hydrangea macrophylla	hydrangea	M	H	H	H	H	H
S	Hydrangea paniculata 'Grandiflora'	peegee hydrangea	M	?	M	?	?	?
S	Hydrangea quercifolia	oakleaf hydrangea	M	?	M	M	H	H
T	Hymenosporum flavum	sweet shade	M	/	M	M	/	/
S	Hypericum beanii	Henry St. John's wort	M	M	M	M	M	?
Gc	Hypericum calycinum	Aaron's beard	M	M	M	M	M	
S	Hypericum 'Hidecote'	St.Johnswort	M	M	M	M	M	
S P	Hypericum moseranum	gold flower	M	M	M	M	M	
P	Iberis sempervirens	evergreen candy tuft	M	M	M	M	M	M
S	Ilex X altaclarensis 'Wilsonii'	Wilson holly	M	M	M	M	M	M
☆ S	Ilex aquifolium	English holly	L	M	M	M	M	M
S	Ilex cornuta 'Burfordii'	Burford holly	L	M	M	M	M	M
S	Ilex dimorphophilla	Okinawan holly	M	M	M	M	/	?
S	Ilex X meserveae	blue boy/girl etc. cvs.	M	M	M	M	/	?
S	Ilex vomitoria	yaupon	L	M	L	L	M	M
P	Impatiens oliveri	poor man's rhododendron	M	/	H	/	/	/
P	Imperata cylindrica 'Rubra'	Japanese blood grass	H	H	M	M	?	M
S	Iochroma cyaneum	tubeflower	M	?	M	M	/	/
P	Ipheion uniflorum (Tritelia)	spring star flower	L	L	L	?	?	?
V	Ipomoea acuminata	blue dawn flower	L	M	L	?	/	M
P	Iris spp.	Douglas iris hybrids	L	L	M	M	/	/
P	Iris spp.	bearded iris	L	L	M	M	M	M

TYPE	BOTANICAL NAME	COMMON NAME	REGIONAL EVALUATIONS					
			1	2	3	4	5	6
P	Iris spp.	Japanese iris	H	H	H	H	/	/
P	Iris spp.	Spanish/Dutch iris	M	M	M	M	M	M
S	Isocoma spp. (Haplopappus)	goldenbush	?	?	VL	VL	VL	VL
Gc	Iva hayesiana	poverty weed	VL	VL	VL	L	/	/
S	Ixora coccinia	jungle geranium	?	?	M	?	/	?
T	Jacaranda mimosifolia	jacaranda	M	M	M	M	/	M
S V	Jasminum angulare	South African jasmine	?	/	M	?	?	?
S	Jasminum floridum	showy jasmine	L	M	M	M	/	M
S	Jasminum humile	Italian jasmine	L	M	M	M	/	M
V	Jasminum leratii	jasmine (leratii)	?	?	M	M	/	/
S	Jasminum mesnyi	primrose jasmine	L	M	M	M	/	M
S	Jasminum nitidum	angel wing jasmine	L	M	M	M	/	M
V	Jasminum polyanthum	pink jasmine	M	M	M	M	/	M
T	Jubaea chilensis	Chilean wine palm	L	M	L	M	/	/
T	Juglans californica	S. California black walnut	L	/	L	L	/	/
T	Juglans hindsii	California black walnut	M	M	/	L	/	/
T	Juglans nigra	eastern black walnut	M	M	/	/	/	/
T	Juglans regia	English walnut	M	M	M	M	/	/
T	Juniperus californica	California juniper	L	L	L	L	L	L
T	Juniperus scopulorum 'Tolleson'	Tolleson's juniper	L	L	M	M	M	M
S Gc	Juniperus spp.	juniper	L	L	L	M	M	M
S	Justicia brandegeana	shrimp plant	M	M	M	M	/	M
S	Justicia californica	chuparosa	?	/	VL	L	L	L
S	Justicia carnea	Brazilian plume flower	M	H	H	H	/	H
S	Justicia sonorea	Sonoran justicia	?	?	?	?	?	L
S	Justicia spicigera	Mexican honeysuckle	/	?	L	M	/	L
P	Kalanchoe spp.	kalanchoe	L	L	L	L	/	M
S	Keckiella antirhinnoides	yellow penstemmon	?	?	L	L	/	/
S V	Keckiella cordifolia	heart-leaved penstemmon	?	?	VL	L	/	/
S	Kerria japonica	Japanese rose	M	M	?	M	M	?
P	Kniphofia uvaria	red hot poker	L	L	L	L	/	M
P	Koelaria glauca	blue hair grass	?	?	M	?	M	?
T	Koelreuteria bipinnata	Chinese flame tree	M	M	M	M	M	M
T	Koelreuteria paniculata	golden rain tree	M	M	M	M	M	M
S	Kolkwitzia amabalis	beauty bush	L	M	M	M	M	/
S	Kunzea spp.	kunzea	L	?	M	?	?	?
T	Laburnum X watereri	golden chain tree	M	M	/	/	/	/
T S	Lagerstroemia indica	crape myrtle	L	L	M	M	M	M
T	Lagunaria patersonii	primrose tree	L	/	L	L	/	/
Gc P	Lamiastrum galeobdolon	yellow archangel	M	M	M	?	?	?
Gc	Lampranthus spp.	ice plant (Lampranthus)	L	L	L	L	/	L
S	Lantana camara	lantana	L	L	L	L	/	M
Gc P	Lantana montevidensis	lantana	L	L	L	L	/	M
S	Larrea tridentata	creosote	VL	VL	VL	L	L	L
P Gc	Laurentia fluviatilis	blue star creeper	M	M	M	M	?	M
T	Laurus nobilis	sweet bay	L	L	L	L	M	M
S P	Lavandula spp.	lavender	L	L	L	L	M	M
S	Lavatera assurgentiflora	tree mallow	L	M	L	L	/	M
S	Lemaireocereus thurbii	organ pipe cactus	/	?	VL	L	/	L
S	Leonotis leonurus	lion's tail	L	L	L	L	M	M
T S	Leptospermum laevigatum	Australian tea tree	L	L	L	L	/	/
S Gc	Leptospermum scoparium	New Zealand tea tree	M	M	L	L	/	/
T	Leucodendron argenteum	Silver tree	L	/	L	/	/	/
S	Leucophyllum spp.	purple sage, Texas ranger etc.	L	L	L	L	L	L
S	Leucospermum cordifolium	nodding pincushion	/	/	L	/	/	/
P	Liatris spicata	gay feather	M	M	M	M	M	M
P	Libertia spp.	libertia	L	?	M	?	?	?
S	Ligustrum japonicum	Japanese privet	M	M	M	M	M	M
T	Ligustrum lucidum	glossy privet	L	L	M	M	M	M

	TYPE	BOTANICAL NAME	COMMON NAME	REGIONAL EVALUATIONS					
				1	2	3	4	5	6
	P	Lilium (garden hybrids)	lily	M	M	M	M	M	M
☆	P	Limonium perezii	statice	L	L	L	M	/	M
	P	Linaria purpurea	toadflax	L	M	L	M	M	M
	T	Liquidambar styraciflua	sweet gum	M	M	M	M	M	/
	T	Liriodendron tulipifera	tulip tree	M	H	M	M	M	/
	P	Lirope muscari	big blue lily turf	M	M	M	M	M	H
	Gc	Lirope spicata	creeping lily turf	M	M	M	M	M	M
	T	Lithocarpus densiflorus	tanbark oak	L	/	L	L	/	/
	P	Lithodora diffusa	heavenly blue	M	M	/	/	/	/
	T	Livistona australis	Australia fountain palm	?	/	M	M	/	/
	T	Livistona chinensis	Chinese fountain palm	?	/	M	M	/	/
	S P	Lobelia laxiflora	Mexican bush lobelia	?	?	VL	VL	?	M
	P	Lobelia richmondensis	perennial lobelia	M	?	M	?	?	?
	V	Lonicera hildebrandiana	giant Burmese honeysuckle	M	M	M	M	M	M
☆	V	Lonicera japonica	Japanese oneysuckle	M	M	L	LL	M	M
☆	V Gc	Lonicera japonica 'Halliana'	Hall's honeysuckle	M	M	L	L	M	M
	S	Lonicera nitida	box honeysuckle	L	M	/	M	/	/
	V	Lonicera sempervirens	trumpet honeysuckle	M	M	/	M	M	M
	S	Lonicera subspicata	chaparral honeysuckle	?	?	/	M	/	/
	T	Lophostemon confertus	Brisbane box	M	/	M	M	/	/
	S	Loropetalum chinense	Chinese witch hazel	L	M	M	?	?	?
☆	Gc	Lotus corniculatus	birdsfoot trefoil	L	M	M	M	/	M
	P	Lotus scoparius	deer weed	VL	?	L	VL	/	/
	S	Luma apiculata	luma	M	?	M	M	/	/
	S	Lupinus albifrons	silver lupine	VL	L	/	L	/	/
★	S	Lupinus arboreus	coastal bush lupine	L	/	L	/	/	/
	P	Lupinus (Russell hybrids)	Russell lupines	M	M	/	/	/	/
	P	Lychnis chalcedonica	Maltese cross	?	?	M	M	M	M
	P	Lychnis coronaria	rose campion/crown pink	L	L	L	L	M	M
	S	Lycianthus rantonnetii	Paraguay nightshade/ blue potato bush	M	M	M	M	/	M
	T	Lyonothamnus floribunda	Catalina ironwood	L	/	VL	L	/	/
	T S	Lysiloma candida	palo blanca	/	/	?	?	/	M
	T S	Lysiloma thornberi	feather bush	?	/	L	?	/	M
	Gc	Lysimachia nummularia	moneywort	H	H	H	H	/	/
	T	Macadamia spp.	macadamia nut	M	/	M	M	/	/
	V	Macfadyena unguis-cati	cat's claw	L	L	L	L	L	L
	S	Mackaya bella	mackaya	M	?	M	M	/	/
	P	Macleaya spp.	plume poppy	M	?	M	?	?	?
	T	Magnolia grandiflora	southern magnolia	M	M	M	M	/	H
	T	Magnolia soulangeana	saucer magnolia	M	M	M	M	M	/
	T	Magnolia stellata	star magnolia	M	M	M	M	M	/
	S	Mahonia aquifolium	Oregon grape	M	M	M	M	M	M
	S	Mahonia bealei	leatherleaf mahonia	M	M	M	M	M	M
	S	Mahonia 'Golden Abundance'	golden abundance mahonia	L	L	L	M	M	M
	S	Mahonia lomariifolia	Chinese holly grape	M	M	L	M	M	M
	S	Mahonia nevinii	Nevin mahonia	VL	L	L	L	M	M
	S	Mahonia pinnata	California holly grape	L	L	M	M	M	M
	Gc	Mahonia repens	creeping mahonia	L	L	L	M	M	/
	S	Malacothamnus fasciculatus	bush mallow	L	?	VL	L	/	/
	Gc	Maleophora spp.	ice plant (Maleophora)	L	L	L	L	/	L
	S	Malosma laurina (Rhus laurina)	laurel sumac	VL	L	VL	L	/	/
	T	Malus spp.(edible)	apple	M	M	M	M	M	/
	T	Malus spp. eg. 'Robinson'	crabapple	M	M	/	M	M	/
	V	Mandevilla laxa	Chilean jasmine	M	/	M	M	/	M
	S	Mandevilla splendens	mandevilla	M	/	M	M	/	M
	V	Mandevilla cvs.	'Alice Dupont' etc.	M	/	M	H	/	H
	T	Markhamia hildebrandtii	markhamia	?	?	M	/	/	/
	V	Mascagnia lilacina	purple orchid vine	?	?	?	?	?	M

TYPE	BOTANICAL NAME	COMMON NAME	REGIONAL EVALUATIONS					
			1	2	3	4	5	6
V	Mascagnia macroptera	yellow orchid vine	?	?	?	?	?	M
V	Maurandya antirriniflora	snapdragon vine	?	?	M	?	/	M
T	Maytenus boaria	mayten tree	M	M	M	M	/	/
P	Mazus reptans	mazus	M	?	M	H	?	?
T S	Melaleuca armillaris	bracelet honey-myrtle	VL	?	L	M	/	M
T S	Melaleuca decussata	totem poles (lilac melaleuca)	VL	?	L	M	/	M
T S	Melaleuca elliptica	granite honey-myrtle	VL	?	L	M	/	M
S	Melaleuca fulgens	melaleuca (fulgens)	?	?	L	M	/	M
S	Melaleuca huegelii	chenile honey-myrtle	?	?	L	M	/	M
S	Melaleuca incana	grey honey-myrtle	?	?	L	M	/	M
T	Melaleuca lanceolata	black tea	?	L	?	L	/	/
T	Melaleuca linariifolia	flax leaf paper bark	L	L	L	L	/	/
T	Melaleuca nesophila	pink melaleuca	L	L	L	L	/	/
T	Melaleuca quinquenervia	cajeput tree	L	L	M	M	/	M
T	Melaleuca rhaphiophylla	swamp paper bark	?	L	?	L	/	/
T	Melaleuca squamea	swamp honey-myrtle	?	?	L	M	/	M
T	Melaleuca styphelioides	melaleuca (styphelioides)	L	L	L	M	/	M
P	Melampodium leucanthum	blackfoot daisy	L	/	?	L	L	L
T	Melia azedarach	chinaberry	VL	L	VL	L	L	L
S	Melianthus major	honey bush	L	M	M	M	/	M
Gc P	Mentha spp.	mint	L	L	M	M	M	M
V	Merremia aurea	merremia (aurea)	?	?	?	?	/	M
V	Merremia quinquefolia	merremia (quinquefolia)	?	?	?	?	/	M
T	Metasequoia glyptostroboides	dawn redwood	H	H	H	H	/	/
T	Metrosideros excelsus	New Zealand Christmas tree	L	/	M	M	/	/
T	Michelia doltsopa	wong-lan	M	M	M	M	/	/
S	Michelia figo	banana shrub	M	?	M	H	/	H
P	Microlepia strigosa	lace fern	M	/	M	H	/	/
V	Milletia reticulata	evergreen wisteria	?	?	M	M	/	/
S	Mimulus spp. (Diplacus)	monkey flower	L	L	L	L	/	/
P	Mirabilis jalapa	four o'clock	L	L	/	L	M	M
P	Miscanthus sinensis	eulalia grass	M	M	M	M	M	M
P	Miscanthus transmorrisonensis	evergreen eulalia	?	?	M	?	M	M
P	Monarda didyma	bee balm	M	M	M	M	M	M
P	Monardella villosa	coyote mint	VL	VL	VL	L	?	M
T	Morus alba	white mulberry	M	M	M	M	M	M
Gc V	Muehlenbeckia axillaris	creeping wire vine	M	M	M	M	/	M
Gc V	Muehlenbeckia complexa	mattress vine	L	L	M	M	/	M
P	Muhlenbergia capillaris	hairy awn muhly	?	?	M	?	M	M
P	Muhlenbergia dumosa	bamboo muhly	L	?	M	M	M	M
P	Muhlenbergia rigens	deer grass	L	?	L	M	M	M
S	Murraya paniculata	orange jessamine	/	H	M	M	/	M
S P	Musa spp.	banana	H	H	H	H	/	M
☆ T S	Myoporum laetum	myoporum	L	M	M	M	/	/
S Gc	Myoporum X 'Pacificum'	pacifica saltbush	L	L	L	L	/	/
S Gc	Myoporum parvifolium	myoporum	L	L	L	L	/	M
S Gc	Myoporum 'South Coast'	south coast myoporum	L	L	L	M	/	/
☆ P	Myosotis scorpioides	forget-me-not	M	M	/	M	/	H
S	Myrica californica	Pacific wax myrtle	L	L	L	M	/	/
S	Myrsine africana	African boxwood	L	L	L	M	/	/
S	Myrtus communis	true myrtle	L	L	L	M	M	M
S	Nandina domestica	heavenly bamboo	L	L	L	M	M	M
S	Nandina domestica 'Purpurea'	heavenly bamboo (Nana)	M	M	M	M	M	M
P	Narcissus spp.	daffodil	VL	VL	L	L	L	L
T	Neodypsis decaryi	triangle palm	?	/	M	?	/	/
P	Nepeta X faassenii	catmint	L	M	M	M	M	M
P	Nephrolepis cordifolia	southern sword fern	M	M	M	M	M	M
P	Nephrolepis exaltata	sword fern	/	M	M	M	M	M
P	Nerine spp.	nerine	L	L	L	?	M	M

	TYPE	BOTANICAL NAME	COMMON NAME	REGIONAL EVALUATIONS					
				1	2	3	4	5	6
☆	S	Nerium oleander	oleander	L	L	L	L	M	M
	P	Nierembergia hippomanica	cup flower	M	M	M	M	/	M
	S P	Nolina spp.	bear grass	?	VL	VL	VL	L	L
	T	Nyssa sylvatica	sour gum/tupelo	M	M	M	H	/	/
	S	Ochna serrulata	bird's eye bush	L	/	M	M	/	/
	Gc P	Oenothera berlandieri	Mexican evening primrose	L	L	L	L	M	M
	P	Oenothera caespitosa	tufted (white) evening primrose	?	?	/	L	L	L
	Gc P	Oenothera cheirianthifolia	beach evening primrose	?	?	VL	/	/	/
	Gc P	Oenothera stubbei	Baja evening primrose	L	L	L	L	M	M
☆	T	Olea europaea	olive	VL	VL	L	L	M	M
	T	Olmediella betschleriana	Guatemalan holly	M	/	M	M	/	/
	T	Olneya tesota	desert ironwood	/	/	L	/	L	L
	P	Ophiopogon jaburan	giant lily turf	L	M	M	M	M	M
	P	Ophiopogan japonicum	mondo grass	M	M	H	H	H	H
	S	Opuntia spp.	prickly pear/cholla	VL	VL	VL	L	L	L
	P	Oreganum spp.	dittany/oregano etc.	M	M	L	L	?	?
	S	Osmanthus fragrans	sweet olive	M	M	M	M	M	M
	S	Osmanthus heterophyllus	holly leaf osmanthus	M	M	M	M	M	M
	Gc	Osteospermum spp.	African daisy	L	L	L	L	/	M
	V	Oxera pulchella	royal climber	?	/	M	M	/	/
	P	Oxypetalum caeruleum	tweedia	?	?	M	?	?	?
	T	Pachycormis discolor	elephant tree	?	?	VL	?	?	L
	Gc	Pachysandra terminalis	Japanese spurge	M	M	M	/	M	/
	P	Paeonia spp.	peony	M	M	/	/	/	/
	V	Pandorea jasminoides	bower vine	M	/	M	M	/	/
	V	Pandorea pandorana	wonga wonga vine	M	/	M	M	/	/
	P	Papaver orientale	oriental poppy	M	M	M	M	M	H
	P	Parahebe perfoliata	parahebe	?	?	M	?	?	?
	T	Parkinsonia aculeata	Mexican palo verde/Jerusalem thorn	VL	VL	L	L	L	L
	Gc V	Parthenocissus quinquefolia	Virginia creeper	M	M	M	M	M	M
	Gc V	Parthenocissus tricuspidata	Boston ivy	M	M	M	M	M	M
	V	Passiflora spp.	passion vine	M	M	M	M	/	M
	P	Pelargonium domesticum	Martha Washington pelargonium	M	M	M	M	/	M
	P	Pelargonium hortorum	garden geranium	L	L	M	M	/	M
	Gc P	Pelargonium peltatum	ivy geranium	M	M	M	M	/	M
	P	Pennisetum alopecuroides	Chinese pennisetum	L	L	L	L	L	L
★	P	Pennisetum setaceum	fountain grass	L	VL	L	L	L	L
	P	Pennisetum setaceum 'Cupreum'	purple fountain grass	L	L	L	L	L	L
	P	Penstemon hybrids	penstemon (hybrids)	M	M	M	M	M	M
	P	Penstemon wild spp.	penstemon (wild)	L	L	L	L	L	L
	S P	Perovskia spp.	Russian sage	M	M	M	M	/	/
	T	Persea americana	avocado	M	M	M	M	M	/
	V	Petrea volubilis	queens wreath	?	?	M	M	?	?
	P	Phalaris spp. (ornamental)	ribbon grass	M	M	M	M	/	/
	S	Philadelphus mexicanus	evergreen mock orange	L	M	M	M	M	M
	S	Philadelphus X virginalis	double mock orange	M	M	M	/	/	/
	S P	Philodendron selloum	philodendron	M	M	M	M	/	M
	S P	Phlomis fruticosa	Jerusalem sage	L	L	L	L	M	M
	P	Phlox (shrubby cvs.)	phlox	M	M	M	M	M	M
	Gc P	Phlox subulata	moss pink	M	M	/	/	M	M
	T	Phoenix canariensis	Canary Island date palm	L	L	L	L	M	M
	T	Phoenix dactylifera	date palm	L	L	L	L	M	M
	T	Phoenix reclinata	Senegal date palm	/	/	M	M	/	M
	T	Phoenix roebelenii	pigmy date palm	/	/	M	M	/	M
	T	Phoenix rupicola	cliff date palm	/	/	M	M	/	/
	S	Phormium hybrids	flax	L	M	M	M	/	M
	S	Phormium tenax	New Zealand flax	L	L	L	M	/	M
	T S	Photinia X fraseri	Fraser photinia	M	M	M	M	M	M

TYPE	BOTANICAL NAME	COMMON NAME	REGIONAL EVALUATIONS					
			1	2	3	4	5	6
T S	Photinia serrulata	Chinese photinia	M	M	/	M	M	M
✿ Gc	Phyla nodiflora	lippia	L	M	L	L	/	M
S	Phyllostachys spp.	bamboo (Phylostachys)	L	L	M	M	M	M
P	Physostegia virginiana	obedience plant	M	M	M	M	M	M
T	Picea abies	Norway spruce	M	M	M	/	/	/
T	Picea pungens	Colorado spruce	M	M	M	/	/	/
S	Pieris forestii	Chinese pieris	M	M	/	/	/	/
S	Pieris japonica	lily-of-the-valley shrub	M	M	/	/	/	/
T	Pinus attenuata	knobcone pine	L	L	L	L	/	/
T	Pinus X attenuradiata	knobkone-Monterrey pine	M	/	L	M	/	/
T	Pinus brutia	Calabrian pine	L	L	L	L	M	M
T	Pinus canariensis	Canary Island pine	L	L	L	M	M	M
T	Pinus contorta	beach pine	M	M	/	/	/	/
T	Pinus coulteri	Coulter pine	L	L	L	L	M	/
T	Pinus densiflora	Japanese red pine	M	M	/	M	/	/
T	Pinus edulis	pinyon pine	L	L	VL	L	L	/
T	Pinus eldarica	eldarica pine	L	L	L	L	M	M
T	Pinus halepensis	Aleppo pine	L	L	L	L	L	L
T	Pinus jeffreyi	Jeffrey pine	L	L	/	/	/	/
T	Pinus monophylla	single leaf pinyon pine	L	/	L	L	L	/
T	Pinus montezumae	Montezuma pine	L	?	L	L	/	/
S	Pinus mugo	mugo pine	L	L	/	M	M	/
T	Pinus muricata	bishop pine	M	M	L	/	/	/
T	Pinus nigra	Austrian black pine	M	M	/	M	M	/
T	Pinus patula	Jelecote pine	M	M	M	M	M	M
✿ T	Pinus pinaster	cluster pine	M	M	L	/	/	/
✿ T	Pinus pinea	Italian stone pine	L	L	L	L	M	M
T	Pinus ponderosa	ponderosa pine	L	L	/	L	/	/
✿ T	Pinus radiata	Monterey pine	M	/	M	M	/	/
T	Pinus roxburghii	chir pine	M	M	M	M	M	M
T	Pinus sabiniana	foothill Pine/ Digger Pine	VL	VL	VL	L	/	/
T	Pinus sylvestris	Scotch pine	M	M	/	M	/	/
T	Pinus thunbergiana	Japanese black pine	M	M	M	M	M	M
T	Pinus torreyana	Torrey pine	L	L	L	M	/	/
T	Pisonia umbellifera	bird catcher tree	?	/	M	?	/	/
T	Pistacia chinensis	Chinese pistache	L	L	M	M	M	M
T	Pistacia vera	pistachio	L	L	M	M	/	/
T	Pithecellobium flexicaule	Texas ebony	?	?	/	?	/	L
T	Pithecellobium pallens	tenaza	?	?	?	?	L	L
T S	Pittosporum crassifolium	evergreen pittosporum	M	M	M	M	/	/
T S	Pittosporum eugenioides	tarata	M	M	M	M	/	/
T	Pittosporum phillyraeoides	willow pittosporum	M	M	L	L	/	M
T S	Pittosporum rhombifolium	Queensland pittosporum	/	/	M	M	/	/
T S	Pittosporum tenuifolium	tawhiwhi	M	M	M	M	/	/
S	Pittosporum tobira	mock orange	L	M	M	M	M	M
S	Pittosporum tobira 'Wheelers Dwarf'	dwarf pittosporum	M	M	M	M	M	M
T	Pittosporum undulatum	victorian box	M	/	M	M	/	/
T	Platanus X acerifolia	London plane	L	L	M	M	H	H
T	Platanus racemosa	California sycamore	M	M	M	M	H	H
T	Platanus wrightii	Arizona sycamore	M	?	M	M	H	H
S	Platycladus orientalis	oriental arborvitae	M	M	M	M	M	M
P	Platycodon grandiflorus	balloon flower	M	M	M	M	M	M
S	Plecostachys serpyllifolia (Helichrysum)	straw flower	L	L	L	L	M	M
S P Gc	Plectranthus spp.	Sweedish ivy	M	/	M	M	/	/
S	Plumbago auriculata	cape plumbago	L	M	M	M	/	M
S	Plumbago scandens	summer snow	?	?	?	M	/	L
S	Plumeria rubra	frangipani	/	/	L	/	/	M

TYPE	BOTANICAL NAME	COMMON NAME	1	2	3	4	5	6
T	Podocarpus gracilior	fern pine	M	M	M	M	/	M
T	Podocarpus henkelii	long leaf yellow wood	M	H	M	M	M	/
T	Podocarpus latifolius	podocarpus (latifolius)	M	?	M	/	/	/
T S	Podocarpus macrophyllus	yew pine	M	M	M	M	M	M
T S	Podocarpus nagi	podocarpus (nagi)	M	M	M	M	M	M
V	Podranea ricasoliana	pink trumpet vine	/	M	M	M	/	M
S	Polygala X dalmaisiana	sweet pea shrub	L	M	M	M	/	/
V	Polygonum aubertii	silver lace vine	L	L	L	L	M	M
Gc	Polygonum capitatum	knotweed	M	M	M	M	M	M
P	Polystichum munitum	sword fern	M	M	M	H	/	H
P	Polystichum polyblepharum	Japanese lace fern	M	H	H	H	M	M
P	Polystichum setiferum	Alaskan fern	M	H	H	H	M	M
T	Populus alba 'Pyramidalis'	bolleana poplar	M	M	M	H	H	H
T	Populus balsamifera	balsam poplar	M	M	M	M	H	H
T	Populus X canadensis	Carolina poplar	H	H	?	M	H	H
T	Populus fremontii	western poplar	M	M	M	M	H	H
T	Populus 'Mohavensis'	Mohave poplar	?	?	?	?	M	M
T	Populus nigra 'Italica'	Lombardy poplar	M	M	M	M	H	H
T	Populus trichocarpa	black cottonwood	H	H	M	M	H	/
S P	Portulacaria afra	elephant's food	L	L	L	L	/	L
S	Potentilla fruticosa cvs.	cinquefoil	M	M	/	/	M	/
Gc	Potentilla tabernaemontanii(verna)	spring cinquefoil	M	M	M	M	/	M
P Gc	Pratia angulata	pratia	?	H	H	H	/	/
T	Prosopis alba	Argentine mesquite	/	L	L	L	M	M
T	Prosopis chilensis	Chilean mesquite	/	L	L	L	M	M
T	Prosopis glandulosa glandulosa	Honey mesquite	/	L	L	L	M	M
T	Prosopis pubescens	screwbean mesquite	/	L	L	L	M	M
T	Prosopis velutina	velvet mesquite	/	L	L	L	M	M
S	Prostanthera rotundifolia	round leaf mint bush	L	M	L	M	/	/
S P	Protea spp.	protea	M	/	M	M	/	/
Gc P	Prunella spp.	self heal	M	M	M	M	?	?
T S	Prunus caroliniana	Carolina laurel cherry	L	L	M	M	M	M
T S	Prunus ilicifolia	holly leaf cherry	L	L	VL	VL	/	/
T S	Prunus lauroceracus	English laurel	M	M	/	H	/	/
T S	Prunus lusitanica	Portugal laurel	L	L	/	/	/	/
T S	Prunus lyonii	Catalina cherry	L	L	L	L	/	/
T	Prunus spp. (edible)	almond	L	M	M	M	M	/
		apricot	M	M	M	M	M	/
T	Prunus spp. (edible)	cherry	M	M	M	M	M	/
		peach	M	M	M	M	M	/
		peach (low chill only)	M	M	M	M	/	M
		nectarine	M	M	M	M	M	/
		plum	M	M	M	M	M	/
		plum (low chill only)	L	M	M	M	/	M
		prune	L	M	M	M	M	/
T	Prunus spp. (ornamental)	flowering cherry	M	M	M	M	M	/
		flowering peach	L	M	M	M	M	/
		flowering plum	L	M	M	M	M	M
T S	Pseudopanax lessonii	pseudopanax	M	?	M	M	/	M
S	Psidium cattleianum	strawberry guava	M	M	M	M	/	M
S	Psidium guajava	common guava	/	/	M	/	/	M
S P	Psilostrophe tagetina	paper flower	?	?	?	L	L	L
P	Pteris spp.	brake fern	M	M	M	H	H	/
P	Pulmonaria officinalis	common lungwort	M	H	M	/	/	/
T	Punica granatum	pomegranate	L	L	M	M	M	M
S	Punica granatum 'Nana'	dwarf pomegranate	L	L	M	M	M	M
P	Puya spp.	puya	VL	?	L	L	/	M
S Gc	Pyracantha spp.	firethorn	L	L	L	M	M	M
V	Pyrostegia venusta	flame vine	/	/	M	M	/	M

TYPE	BOTANICAL NAME	COMMON NAME	REGIONAL EVALUATIONS					
			1	2	3	4	5	6
T	Pyrus calleryana cultivars	Callery pear	M	M	M	M	M	M
T	Pyrus communis	edible pear	M	M	M	M	M	/
T	Pyrus kawakamii	evergreen pear	M	M	M	M	M	M
T	Quercus agrifolia	coast live oak	VL	VL	L	L	/	M
T	Quercus chrysolepis	canyon live oak	VL	L	L	L	/	/
T	Quercus coccinea	scarlet oak	M	M	/	M	/	/
T	Quercus douglasii	blue oak	VL	VL	VL	L	/	/
T S	Quercus dumosa	California scrub oak	VL	VL	VL	VL	L	/
T	Quercus engelmannii	mesa oak	/	L	L	L	/	/
T	Quercus ilex	holly oak	L	L	L	L	M	M
T	Quercus kelloggii	California black oak	L	M	/	M	/	/
T	Quercus lobata	valley oak	L	L	/	M	/	/
T	Quercus muhlenbergii	chinquapin oak	L	?	?	L	L	M
T	Quercus palustris	pin oak	M	M	/	M	/	/
T	Quercus rubra	red oak	M	M	/	M	/	/
T	Quercus shumardii	Shumard red oak	M	M	?	/	/	/
T	Quercus suber	cork oak	L	L	L	L	L	L
T	Quercus texana	Texas red oak	L	?	?	L	L	M
T	Quercus tomentella	island oak	L	?	L	/	/	/
T	Quercus virginiana	southern live oak	M	M	M	M	M	M
T	Quercus wislizeni	interior live oak	VL	VL	VL	VL	M	/
T	Radermachera sinica	radermachera	/	/	M	/	/	/
T	Ravanea rivularis	ravanea	/	?	M	M	/	/
P	Rehmannia elata	rehmannia	H	H	M	H	M	M
Gc	Rhagodia deltophylla	rhagodia	?	?	VL	?	?	?
S	Rhamnus alaternus	Italian buckthorn	L	L	L	M	/	/
S	Rhamnus californica	coffeeberry	L	L	VL	L	/	M
S	Rhamnus crocea	redberry	L	L	VL	L	/	M
S	Rhamnus crocea ilicifolia	hollyleaf redberry	L	L	VL	L	/	M
S	Rhaphiolepis spp.	Indian hawthorne	L	L	M	M	M	M
T	Rhaphiolepis 'Majestic Beauty'	majestic beauty	L	L	M	M	M	M
S	Rhapis excelsa	lady palm	/	/	M	M	/	/
S	Rhododendron spp.	azalea	M	M	H	H	/	/
S	Rhododendron spp.	rhododendron	M	M	H	H	/	/
V	Rhoicissus capensis	evergreen grape	M	/	M	M	/	M
T S	Rhopalostylis baueri	Norfolk palm	?	/	M	M	/	/
T S	Rhopalostylis sapida	Nikau palm	?	/	H	H	/	/
S	Rhus integrifolia	lemonade berry	L	L	VL	L	/	/
T	Rhus lancea	African sumac	L	L	L	L	M	M
T	Rhus lanceolata	prairie flameleaf sumac	?	?	?	?	L	L
	Rhus laurina (see Malosma laurina)							
S	Rhus ovata	sugar bush	L	L	VL	L	M	M
S	Rhus trilobata	squawbush	L	L	L	L	L	/
S T	Rhus typhina	staghorn sumac	L	L	L	?	L	/
S	Ribes aureum	golden currant	L	L	L	L	L	/
S	Ribes indecorum	white flowering currant	L	L	L	L	L	/
S	Ribes malvaceum	chaparral currant	VL	VL	VL	L	/	/
S	Ribes sanguineum	red flowering currant	L	L	L	M	/	/
S	Ribes speciosum	fuchsia flowering gooseberry	L	L	L	M	/	/
S Gc	Ribes viburnifolium	evergreen currant	L	L	L	M	/	/
T	Robinia X ambigua	locust	L	L	L	L	M	M
T	Robinia pseudoacacia	black locust	L	L	L	L	L	L
S P	Romneya coulteri	Matilija poppy	VL	VL	VL	L	/	/
V	Rosa banksiae	Lady Banks rose	LL	L	M	M	M	M
S	Rosa californica	California wild rose	L	L	L	L	/	/
V	Rosa 'Cecile Brunner'	Cecile Brunner rose	L	L	M	M	M	M
S	Rosa hybrids..bush	rose	M	M	M	M	H	H
V	Rosa hybrids..climbing	climbing roses	M	M	M	M	H	H
S P	Rosmarinus officinalis	rosemary	L	L	L	L	M	M

TYPE	BOTANICAL NAME	COMMON NAME	REGIONAL EVALUATIONS					
			1	2	3	4	5	6
P Gc	Rosemarinus 'Prostratus'	trailing rosemary	L	L	L	M	M	M
S Gc	Rubus calycinoides	bramble	M	M	M	/	/	/
S	Ruellia californica	rama parda	?	?	VL	VL	/	L
S	Ruellia peninsularis	Baja ruellia	/	?	M	M	/	M
P	Rumohra adiantiformis	leather leaf fern	M	M	M	M	/	/
T	Sabal spp.	palmetto	/	/	M	M	/	/
Gc P	Sagina subulata	Irish moss	M	M	M	H	H	H
Gc P	Sagina subulata 'Aurea'	Scotch moss	M	M	M	H	H	H
T S	Salix spp.	willow	H	H	H	H	H	H
S	Salvia apiana	white sage	?	?	VL	VL	L	L
S	Salvia chamaedroides	blue sage	?	L	L	L	/	M
S	Salvia clevelandii	Cleveland sage	L	L	VL	L	/	L
P	Salvia coccinea	Texas sage	L	M	M	M	M	M
P	Salvia dorrii	purple sage	?	M	?	?	M	M
P	Salvia farinacea	nealy cup sage	M	M	M	M	/	M
S	Salvia greggii	autumn sage	L	L	L	L	M	M
S	Salvia leucantha	Mexican bush sage	L	L	L	L	/	M
S	Salvia leucophylla	purple sage	L	/	L	L	/	M
S Gc	Salvia melifera	black sage	L	L	L	L	/	?
S	Salvia microphylla	salvia (microphylla)	?	M	L	M	L	L
S	Salvia munzii	San Miguel Mountain sage	?	?	VL	L	L	/
P	Salvia officinalis	garden sage	L	M	M	M	M	M
S	Salvia uliginosa	bog sage	M	M	M	?	/	/
T S	Sambucus spp.	elderberry	L	L	L	L	M	M
S P	Santolina spp.	lavender cotton	L	L	L	L	L	L
T	Sapium sebiferum	Chinese tallow tree	M	M	M	M	/	/
Gc P	Saponaria ocymoides	saponaria	L	L	M	M	/	/
S Gc	Sarcococca hookerana humilis	sweet sarcococca	M	M	M	M	M	M
S	Sarcococca ruscifolia	fragrant sarcococca	M	M	M	M	M	M
S	Sasa spp.	bamboo (Sasa)	L	L	M	M	/	M
P	Saxifraga spp.	saxifrage	M	M	M	H	H	H
P	Scabiosa spp.	pincushion flower	M	M	M	M	M	M
Gc P	Scaevola aemula 'Diamond Head'	blue wonder	L	L	M	M	/	/
Gc P	Scaevola 'Mauve Clusters'	fan flower	L	L	M	M	/	/
S	Schefflera actinophylla (see Brassaia actinophylla)							
S	Schefflera arboricola	Hawaiian elf schefflera	/	/	H	H	/	H
T S	Schefflera pueckleri (Tupidanthus)	Australian umbrella tree	/	/	M	H	/	H
T	Schinus molle	California pepper tree	VL	L	VL	L	M	M
T	Schinus polygamous	Peruvian pepper	VL	L	L	L	L	M
T	Schinus terebinthefolius	Brazilian pepper tree	M	M	M	M	/	M
T	Schotia latifolia	forest Boer bloom	?	?	M	?	?	?
P Gc	Sedum spp.	stone crop	L	L	L	L	L	L
P	Sempervivum spp.	house leek	L	L	L	L	/	L
P	Senecio cineraria	dusty miller	L	L	L	L	/	M
S	Senecio douglasii	bush groundsel	?	?	L	L	/	M
Gc	Senecio mandraliscae	kleinia	/	/	L	M	/	M
T	Sequoia sempervirens	coast redwood	H	H	H	H	/	/
T	Sequoiadendron giganteum	giant sequoia	M	M	/	M	/	/
P	Sesleria spp.	moor grass	?	?	M	?	/	/
P	Setcreasea pallida 'Purple Heart'	purple heart setcreasea	/	/	M	M	H	H
S	Shepherdia argentea	silver buffaloberry	?	?	VL	VL	?	?
P	Silene spp.	moss pink/campion	?	?	L	L	?	M
S	Simmondsia chinensis	jojoba	VL	VL	VL	VL	L	L
P	Sisyrinchium bellum	blue-eyed grass	VL	VL	L	L	M	M
P	Sisyrinchium californicum	golden-eyed grass	M	M	M	M	M	M
P	Sisysrinchium striatum	sisysrinchium (striatum)	M	?	M	?	/	/
V	Solandra maxima	cup of gold vine	M	M	M	M	/	/
V	Solanum jasminoides	potato vine	M	M	M	M	/	M

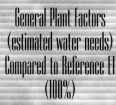

TYPE	BOTANICAL NAME	COMMON NAME	REGIONAL EVALUATIONS					
			1	2	3	4	5	6
V	Solanum wendlandii	Costa Rican nightshade	L	/	M	/	/	M
Gc P	Soleirolia soleroli	baby's tears	H	H	H	H	/	H
S Gc	Sollya heterophylla	Australian bluebell creeper	L	L	L	L	/	/
T	Sophora japonica	Japanese pagoda tree	L	L	M	M	M	M
T S	Sophora secundiflora	Texas mountain laurel	L	L	L	L	M	M
T	Sorbus aucuparia	European mountain ash	/	M	/	/	M	M
✶ S	Spartium junceum	Spanish broom	/	VL	VL	L	/	/
P	Spathiphyllum spp.	spathiphyllum	/	/	H	/	/	/
T	Spathodea campanulata	African tulip tree	/	/	M	/	/	/
P	Sphaeralcea spp.	desert/globe mallow	L	L	L	L	/	L
S	Spiraea spp.	spiraea	M	M	M	M	M	M
P	Sprekelia formosissima	Aztec lily	L	L	L	L	L	L
P	Stachys bysantina	lamb's ears	L	L	M	M	/	M
T	Stenocarpus sinuatus	firewheel tree	/	/	M	M	/	/
V	Stephanotis floribunda	Madagascar jasmine	/	/	M	M	/	M
P	Stipa lepida	foothill stipa	VL	VL	L	L	L	L
P	Stipa pulchra	feather grass	VL	L	VL	L	L	L
P	Stipa stipa spinosa	desert bunch grass	?	?	L	L	L	L
P	Stokesia laevis	stokes aster	M	M	M	M	M	M
T	Strelitzia nicolai	giant bird of paradise	M	/	M	M	/	M
S	Strelitzia reginae	bird of paradise	M	M	M	M	/	M
S	Streptosolen jamesonii	marmalade bush	/	/	M	H	/	/
T	Styrax japonicus	Japanese snowbell	M	M	/	/	M	/
S	Styrax officinalis californicus	California storax	L	L	L	L	M	/
S	Syringa vulgaris	lilac	M	M	/	M	M	/
S	Syzygium paniculatum	Australian brush cherry	M	M	M	M	/	/
T	Tabebuia chrysotricha	golden trumpet tree	?	/	M	M	/	M
T	Tabebuia impetiginosa	pink/lavender trumpet tree	/	/	M	M	/	/
S P	Tagetes lemmoni	mountain marigold	L	L	L	L	M	M
P	Tagetes lucida	Mexican tarragon	?	M	M	M	M	M
✶ T S	Tamarix spp.	tamarisk	VL	VL	/	L	L	L
T	Taxodium distichum	bald cypress	M	/	M	M	/	/
T	Taxodium mucronatum	Montezuma cypress	M	?	M	M	/	/
T S	Taxus baccata	English yew	M	M	M	M	M	/
T S	Taxus baccata 'Stricta'	Irish yew	M	M	M	M	M	/
T S	Tecoma stans	yellow bells	/	/	M	M	M	M
S	Tecoma 'Orange Jubilee'	orange jubilee tecoma	M	M	?	?	/	M
S V	Tecomaria capensis	cape honeysuckle	M	M	M	M	/	M
S	Ternstroemia gymnanthera	ternstroemia	M	M	M	M	M	/
S	Tetrapanax papyrifer	rice paper plant	L	M	M	M	/	M
V	Tetrastigma voinieranum	Javan grape	/	/	M	M	/	M
Gc	Teucrium chamaedrys	germander	L	L	L	L	M	M
P Gc	Teucrium cossonii	Majorcan germander	VL	L	L	L	/	L
S	Teucrium fruticans	bush germander	L	L	L	L	/	M
P	Thalictrum polycarpum	medow rue	M	?	M	M	M	M
T S	Thevetia peruviana	yellow oleander	/	/	M	M	/	M
T	Thevetia thevetioides	giant thevetia	/	/	M	M	/	M
S	Thuja occidentalis	American arborvitae	M	M	/	M	M	M
V	Thunbergia grandiflora	sky flower	M	/	M	/	/	M
V	Thunbergia gregorii	orange clock vine	M	/	M	M	/	M
GC P	Thymus spp.	thyme	M	M	M	M	M	M
S	Tibouchina urvilleana	princess flower	M	/	M	H	/	H
T	Tilia americana	American linden	M	M	/	/	/	/
T	Tilia cordata	little leaf linden	M	M	/	/	/	/
T	Tipuana tipu	tipu tree	M	/	M	M	/	/
Gc V	Trachelospermum asiaticum	Asian star jasmine	M	M	M	M	M	M
S Gc V	Trachelospermum jasminoides	star jasmine	M	M	M	M	M	M
T	Trachycarpus fortunei	windmill palm	L	M	M	M	M	/

TYPE	BOTANICAL NAME	COMMON NAME	1	2	3	4	5	6
P	Tradescantia andersoniana	spiderwort	M	M	M	M	M	M
S	Trichocereus spp.	torch cactus	?	?	L	?	L	L
S P	Trichostema lanatum	woolly blue curls	VL	VL	VL	L	/	M
S P	Trichostema parishii	mountain blue curls	?	?	VL	L	/	/
Gc	Trifolium fragiferum O'Connor	O'Connor's legume	M	M	M	M	M	M
	Tristania conferta (See Lophostemon confertus)							
	Tristania laurina (See Tristaniopsis laurina)							
T	Tristaniopsis laurina	little leaf myrtle	M	/	M	M	/	/
P	Trollius spp.	globeflower	?	H	M	M	H	H
P	Tropaeolum majus ☆	nasturtium	M	M	/	M	/	M
P	Tulbaghia fragrans	sweet garlic	M	M	M	M	/	M
P	Tulbaghia violacea	society garlic	M	M	M	M	/	M
	Tupidanthus calyptratus (See Schefflera pueckleri)							
T	Ulmus americana	American elm	M	M	/	/	/	/
T	Ulmus parvifolia	Chinese evergreen elm	M	M	M	M	M	M
T	Ulmus pumila	Siberian elm	L	L	/	L	M	M
T	Umbellularia californica	California bay	M	M	M	M	/	/
S	Vaccinium ovatum	evergreen huckleberry	M	M	/	/	/	/
S	Vaccinium parvifolium	red huckleberry	M	M	/	/	/	/
S	Vauquelinia californica	Arizona rosewood	L	?	/	/	M	M
S	Vequiera deltoidea	golden eye	?	?	?	/	L	L
P	Verbascum phoeniceum	purple mullein	L	L	L	L	/	/
P	Verbena bonariensis	verbena (bonariensis)	VL	M	L	L	M	M
Gc P	Verbena gooddingii	Goodding verbena	L	L	L	L	/	M
P	Verbena hybrids	garden verbena	L	L	M	M	/	M
Gc P	Verbena lilacina	lilac verbena	?	?	L	L	/	L
Gc	Verbena peruviana	Peruvian verbena	L	L	L	L	/	M
Gc P	Verbena rigida	vervian	?	M	M	M	/	M
Gc	Verbena stricta	hoary vervian	L	M	M	M	M	M
Gc	Verbena tenera (pulchella)	rock verbena	?	?	?	M	M	M
Gc	Verbena tenuisecta	moss verbena	L	L	L	L	/	M
P	Veronica spp.	veronica	M	M	M	/	/	M
Gc	Veronica repens	speedwell	M	M	M	/	/	/
S	Viburnum burkwoodii	Burkwood viburnum	L	M	M	/	M	/
S	Viburnum davidii	David viburnum	M	M	/	/	M	/
S	Viburnum japonicum	Japanese viburnum	M	M	M	M	M	/
S	Viburnum odoratissimum	sweet viburnum	L	M	M	/	M	/
S	Viburnum opulus	European cranberry bush	L	M	M	M	M	/
S	Viburnum rhytidophyllum	leatherleaf viburnum	M	M	M	M	M	/
S	Viburnum suspensum	sadanqua viburnum	M	M	M	M	M	M
S	Viburnum tinus	laurustinus	M	M	M	M	M	M
V	Vigna caracalla	snail vine	M	/	M	M	/	M
T	Villebrunea pedunculata	villebrunea	?	?	M	?	?	?
Gc	Vinca major ★	periwinkle	M	M	M	M	M	M
Gc	Vinca minor	periwinkle	M	M	M	M	M	M
Gc	Viola hederacea	Australian violet	M	M	M	H	M	M
Gc	Viola labradorica	viola	M	M	M	H	H	H
Gc P	Viola odorata	sweet violet	M	M	M	H	H	H
T	Vitex agnus-castus	chaste tree	L	L	L	M	M	M
V	Vitis californica	California wild grape	M	M	VL	L	M	M
V	Vitis girdiana	desert grape	?	M	L	L	M	M
V	Vitis labrusca	American grape	L	L	L	M	M	M
V	Vitis vinifera	European grape	L	L	M	M	M	M
T	Washingtonia filifera	California fan palm	L	M	L	L	M	M
T	Washingtonia robusta	Mexican fan palm	L	M	L	L	M	M
P	Watsonia spp. ☆	watsonia	L	M	L	M	M	M

Column header: REGIONAL EVALUATIONS (1 2 3 4 5 6)

TYPE	BOTANICAL NAME	COMMON NAME	REGIONAL EVALUATIONS					
			1	2	3	4	5	6
P Gc	Wedelia trilobata	trailing daisy	?	?	H	H	?	?
S	Weigela florida	weigelia	M	M	M	M	M	/
S	Westringia fruticosa	coast rosemary	L	L	L	L	/	M
V	Wisteria spp.	wisteria	M	M	M	M	M	M
P	Woodwardia fimbriata	giant chain fern	M	M	M	M	/	/
P	Woodwardia radicans	European chain fern	H	/	H	H	H	H
P	Xanthorrhoea spp.	grass tree	L	/	L	L	?	?
S P	Xylococcus bicolor	mission manzanita	?	?	VL	L	M	/
S	Xylosma congestum	shiny xylosma	L	L	M	M	M	M
S T	Yucca spp.	yucca	L	L	L	L	L	L
S	Zamia pumila	sago cycas	/	/	M	H	/	/
☆ P	Zantedeschia aethiopia	calla	M	M	M	H	H	M
P	Zauschneria spp. (see Epilobium)							
T	Zelkova serrata	saw leaf zelkova	M	M	L	M	M	M
P	Zephryranthes spp.	zephyr flower	M	M	M	M	/	/
GC P	Zinnia grandiflora	prairie zinnia	M	M	M	M	M	M
T	Ziziphus jujuba	Chinese jujube	L	L	L	M	M	M
Gc P	Zoyzia tenuifolia	Mascarene grass	M	M	M	M	M	M

APPENDICES VI

Cooperative Extension County Offices

ALAMEDA
224 West Winton Ave., Room 174
Hayward, CA 94544-1220
510-670-5200
510-670-5231 fax

AMADOR
Mail: 108 Court Street
Jackson, CA 95642-2379
Location: 12380 Airport Road
Martell, CA 95654
209-223-6482
209-223-3279 fax

BUTTE
2279B Del Oro Avenue
Oroville, CA 95965-3395
530-538-7201
530-538-7140 fax

CALAVERAS
891 Mountain Ranch Road
County Annex
San Andreas, CA 95249
209-754-6477
209-754-6472 fax

COLUSA
Mail: PO Box 180
Location: 100 Sunrise Blvd., Ste. E
Colusa, CA 95932-0180
530-458-0507
530-458-4625 fax

CONTRA COSTA
75 Santa Barbara Rd., 2nd Floor
Pleasant Hill, CA 94523
510-646-6540
510-646-6708 fax

DEL NORTE
967 H St., Rm.2, Courthouse Annex
Crescent City, CA 95531
707-464-4711
707-464-7520 fax

EL DORADO
311 Fair Lane
Placerville, CA 95667-4101
530-621-5502
530-642-0803 fax

FRESNO
1720 South Maple Avenue
Fresno, CA 93702-4516
209-456-7285
209-456-7575 fax

GLENN
Mail: PO Box 697
Location: County Road 200 E
Orland, CA 95963-0697
530-865-1107
530-865-1109 fax

HUMBOLDT
Agricultural Center Building
5630 South Broadway
Eureka, CA 95503-6999
707-445-7351
707-444-9334 fax

IMPERIAL
1050 East Holton Road
Holtville, CA 92250-9617
760-352-9474
760-352-0846 fax

INYO-MONO
207 West S Street
Bishop, CA 93514
760-873-7854
760-872-1610 fax

KERN
1031 South Mt. Vernon Avenue
Bakersfield, CA 93307-2051
805-868-6200
805-868-6208 fax

KINGS
Mail: 680 N. Campus Dr., Ste. A
Location: Kings County
Agricultural Center
Hanford, CA 93230-3556
209-582-3211, ext. 2730, 2732
209-582-5166 fax

LAKE
Agricultural Center
883 Lakeport Boulevard
Lakeport, CA 95453-5405
707-263-6838
707-263-3963 fax

LASSEN
707 Nevada Street
Susanville, CA 96130-0001
530-257-6363
530-257-6129 fax

LOS ANGELES
2 Coral Ctr.
Monterey Park, CA 91755-7425
213-838-8830
213-838-7449 fax

MADERA
328 Madera Avenue
Madera, CA 93697-5465
209-675-7879
209-675-0639 fax

MARIN
1682 Novato Blvd., Suite 150-B
Novato, CA 94947-7001
415-899-8620
415-899-8619 fax

MARIPOSA
5009 Fairgrounds Road
Mariposa, CA 95338-9435
209-966-2417
209-966-5321 fax

MENDOCINO
Mail: Agricultural Ctr./Courthouse
Location: 579 Low Gap Road
Ukiah, CA 95482-0001
707-463-4495
707-463-4477 fax

MERCED
2145 West Wardrobe Avenue
Merced, CA 95340-6496
209-385-7403
209-722-8856 fax

MODOC
202 West 4th Street
Alturas, CA 96101-3915
530-233-6400, Ext. 400
530-233-3840 fax

MONTEREY
1432 Abbott Street
Salinas, CA 93901-4503
408-759-7350
408-758-3018 fax

NAPA
1710 Soscol Avenue, Suite 4
Napa, CA 94559-1315
707-253-4221 • 707-944-2006
707-253-4434 fax

NEVADA
Veterans Memorial Bldg.
255 S. Auburn Street
Grass Valley, CA 95945-7229
530-273-4563
530-273-4769 fax

ORANGE
1045 Arlington Drive
Costa Mesa, CA 92626-5631
714-708-1606
714-708-2754 fax

PLACER
11477 E Avenue
Auburn, CA 95603-001
530-889-7385
530-889-7397 fax

PLUMAS-SIERRA
208 Fairgrounds Road
Quincy, CA 95971-9462
530-283-6270
530-283-4210 fax

RIVERSIDE
21150 Box Springs Road
Moreno Valley, CA 92557-8718
909-683-6491
909-788-2615 fax

SACRAMENTO
4145 Branch Center Road
Sacramento, CA 95827-3808
916-875-6913
916-875-6233 fax

SAN BENITO
649-A San Benito Street
Hollister, CA 95023-3952
408-637-5346
408-637-7111 fax

SAN BERNARDINO
777 East Rialto Avenue
San Bernardino, CA 92415-0730
909-387-2171
909-387-3306 fax

SAN DIEGO
5555 Overland Avenue, Building 4
San Diego, CA 92123-1719
619-694-2845
619-694-2849 fax

SAN FRANCISCO
300 Piedmont Avenue, Building C
Rm 305-A
San Bruno, CA 94066-3906
415-871-7589
415-871-7399 fax

SAN JOAQUIN
420 South Wilson Way
Stockton, CA 95205-6260
209-468-2085
209-462-5181 fax

SAN LUIS OBISPO
2156 Sierra Way, Suite C
San Luis Obispo, CA 93401-4556
805-781-5940
805-781-4316 fax

SAN MATEO
625 Miramontes Street, Suite 200
Half Moon Bay, CA 94019-1942
650-726-9059
650-726-9267 fax

SANTA BARBARA
Santa Maria Office
Tech Services Building
624 West Foster Road, Suite A
Santa Maria, CA 93455
805-934-6240
805-934-6333 fax

Santa Barbara City Office
105 East Ana-pamu, Suite 5
Santa Barbara, CA 99101
805-568-3300
805-568-3091 fax

SANTA CLARA
1005 Timothy Drive
San Jose, CA 95135
408-299-2635
408-298-5160 fax

SANTA CRUZ
1432 Freedom Boulevard
Watsonville, CA 95076-2741
408-763-8040
408-763-8004 fax

SHASTA
1851 Hartnell Avenue
Redding, CA 96002-2217
530-224-4900
530-224-4904 fax

SISKIYOU
1655 South Main Street
Yreka, CA 96097-9515
530-842-2711
530-842-6931 fax

SOLANO
2000 West Texas Street
Fairfield, CA 94533-4498
707-421-6790
707-429-5532 fax

SONOMA
2604 Ventura Avenue, Room 100-P
Santa Rosa, CA 95403-2894
707-527-2621
707-527-2623 fax

STANISLAUS
733 County Center III Court
Modesto, CA 95355-4400
209-525-6654
209-525-4668 fax

SUTTER-YUBA
142-A Garden Highway
Yuba City, CA 95991-5512
530-822-7515
530-673-5368 fax

TEHAMA
Mail: PO Box 370
Location: 1754 Walnut Street
Red Bluff, CA 96080-0370
530-527-3101
530-527-0917 fax

TRINITY
PO Box 490, County Fairgrounds
Hayfork, CA 96041-0490
530-628-5495
530-648-4171 fax

TULARE
2500 Burrel Avenue
Visalia, CA 93291-4584
209-733-6363
209-733-6720 fax

TUOLUMNE
Mail: 2 South Green Street
Location: 52 North Washington St.
Sonora, CA 95370-4617
209-533-5695
209-532-8978 fax

VENTURA
649 County Square Drive
Ventura, CA 93003-5401
805-645-1451
805-645-1474 Fax

YOLO
70 Cottonwood Street
Woodland, CA 95695-2557
530-666-8143
530-666-8736 fax